None But The Righteous

a novel

Nikita Lynnette Nichols

DORRANCE PUBLISHING CO., INC.
PITTSBURGH, PENNSYLVANIA 15222

For information or to order additional books, please write:
Dorrance Publishing Co., Inc.
701 Smithfield Street
Third Floor
Pittsburgh, Pennsylvania 15222
U.S.A.
1-800-788-7654
Or visit our web site and on-line catalog at www.dorrancepublishing.com

Dedication and Acknowledgments

First and foremost, to the only One that I bow down to. My God who is the Creator and the absolute Love of my life. I praise You for bringing down the strongholds. It feels good to breathe again. You love me like no one else could. I dedicate this book to You!

My wonderful and priceless parents, **William J. and Victoria Nichols**. Time and time again you've picked me up after I've fallen. I can never repay what I owe you, but I promise to try. Thanks for loving me in spite of the choices I made. You two are my greatest inspiration. To the best brother and sister in the entire world, **Raymond Nichols and Theresa Craig**. You've paved the way for me and I thank you for wearing Mom and Dad out because when I was coming up; I got away with everything *(it's safe to admit that now)*. You two spread the sunshine in my life. I am blessed to be your lil' sis.

My aunt in Las Vegas, JoAnn Banks. You make my mother smile and that makes me smile.

My grandfather **Daniel Nichols**, I thank you for the genes. To all of my nieces and nephews, Tabitha, Toiya, Tashea', William II, KenKeith, Amaris, Alexander, Latrice, Martin, Marquis, Michael, Danté, Danielle, Deana, and Christian. You are *all* gems! I had two praying grandmothers, Roberta (Sug) Caridine and Mary (Mother) Johnson. May God rest their souls; I will see them soon.

My fairy godmother, **RoseMary Simmons**. For many years you've placed blessings under my pillow, and I thank you for being real. My godchildren, Kadarryl, Dasierra, and Alexander, I love you so much. My sister-in-law Alesia Nichols, thanks for lending me your ear. My aunties Augustine, Frenchie, Keya, Arnetta, Sandra, Dorothy, Maxine, Arlene, and Ethel. My uncles Tyrone, Douglas, Prince, Kenneth, Nathaniel, Lawrence, Keith, Michael, and Curtis.

Jacqui Beasley, have you started writing yet?

To Edward Primer and *The Voices Of Joy Community Choir*, I love my Monday nights with you guys. Rehearsal is always the bomb. Randy Carter the best drummer ever; where's my Barbie doll? Margaret (Cookie) Hicks, Christopher Johnson, Sebastian Shelton, Fabian Burrell, Curtis and Mary Boyd, Nahanna, Nikki, Starr, thanks for keeping my tresses so pretty. To my peeps at *Progressive Ministries*, Garrick and Gregory, we are three peas in a pod. I look forward to clowning in the Holy Ghost with you guys on Sunday nights. Estella there's a book in you too, I can feel it.

Minister Lavada Kelly, Evangelist Brenda Finley, Jackie Golden, Elder Dollie Sherman, Daphne, Steve Hoover, Elder Richard and Chiffon Perry, Minister Deverrick Crawford, Lola, Linda, Minister Wanda Sharp, Sheila, Evangelist Linda Robinson, Velma, Kamiko, Karla, Toya, Jennifer, Jerome, Lorenzo, Brian, Erica, Tabitha, Deacon G. Donnell Wallace, Ramona, Deacon Ray Paige, Elder Rodney and Evangelist Joyce Dennis; Latoya, Donald (Busta) Woods, Brenda, Ruben, Debra, Esther, and Joyce Foy.

Mark Williams, you're so chocolate, I could eat you up. Margaret, Elaine and Augustine, you are true sisters. Sandra Ward, I love our praise walk in the mornings. Juanita Braggs, you were one of the first to read my manuscript, thanks for having faith in me. Phoebe McKee, Anderson Yancy, Jarvis McCann, Cleavon and Ann Sims, Albert and Kimberly Mitchell, Donna Shea', where are you? My chain divas, Carmen, Cynthia, Deshaun, and Janice, we've crawled many a floor together.

I must send a shout out to C.T.A.'s finest, Charles Walker, Joe McNeal, Reverend Lonnie Rucker, Michael Banks, Dwayne Ellis, Chief, Paul Blakely, Charlie Brown, Leon Fields Jr., Cleo Smith, William Dorsey, Leslie Baughn, Reverend Kenneth Marshall, Jorge Dominguez, Lillian Reyes (you go girl), James Malloy Jr., Frank Desantis, Alice Kinslow, Betty Fisher, Karen Muldrow, Craig Hatch Sr., Lenny Joyce, Kenneth Curtis, Vito Collyard, Anthony Madison, my baby brother Robert (Chris) Baughn, Douglas Johnson and Robert (Duke) Ellington, Joseph Nicosia, Jack Dorsey, and James Payne— you're the best. Pablo, Phil Thibeau, Juanita Payne, Michael Thurman, Keith Lewis, Roscoe Jones, Lorraine Brown, Paul Costa, Allen Marshall, Reverend Joe Garrett, Toi Bowers, Robert Bryan and Jack Himber (You two have literally carried me for more than two years, and I love you for it.)

To the Harrises, Michael, Donell, Ricky, Patricia, Artimese, and Amy: Thanks for the support you gave me throughout the years we shared. My soul sistahs Yolunda Rena' McCann, Malonda Garner, who named one of her twin girls after me; I feel so special. Karen Williams, LaTanya Hicks, Keisha Pierce, Tanya Bell, Kimberly Pierce, Latricia Collins, and Jamia Ray. To my biggest fan down in Belleville, Janet Sprehe. I'll see you at a book signing real soon.

Elder DeAndre Patterson, thanks for writing *(I Made It)* just for me because *I made it and I'm so thankful, I never could've made it this far without the Lord*. To the best and most beautiful First Lady in the world, Gloria Alford **(Lady Glo)**. Thanks for the wisdom you've passed on to me. And I especially thank you for always, always having time to listen to what I have to say.

Dr. T.A. Clark Jr. and Pastor August Minor, I'm sure it's safe to say that you were born to lead all of God's children to righteousness and I personally thank you both for helping me anchor my soul in the Lord. **Apostle Donald L. Alford**, my head shepherd. It wasn't until I sat under your teaching when my gift of writing was revealed to me. Your ministry keeps me focused and it always takes me to the next level. You are an awesome man of God and it's your obedience to Him that makes **Progressive** what it is, thank you.

If by chance I have forgotten anyone, it's not because I'm thoughtless. There are so-o-o many more people spiritually connected with me as I'm connected with God. Please know that Kita loves you too!

Lastly, but most certainly not least, **Minister Randy Gordon**, the one who holds my heart in the palm of his hand. God hasn't created a word that explains what you mean to me, therefore you will never know. I'm so glad it was you and no one else standing in my face when I turned around.

Introduction

Life holds no guarantees. Lynnette Nelson's life was no exception.

She had it all, wonderful parents who cared for her deeply, a job that allowed her to do what she did best (help people in need), a church home where she worshiped and praised God like there was no tomorrow, and many friends and loved ones whose lives were inspired through her singing ministry. Her life was complete. God had blessed her abundantly. Lynnette thought that if she asked Him for one more thing, she would appear to be greedy. If He never did anything else for Lynnette, what He had done already was enough.

Then Gerald Hawkins enters her life and turns it upside down and inside out. She marries him, then tries to hold on to him, and keep her sanity at the same time. Lynnette loves her husband, but does he love her?

Journey with Lynnette Nelson-Hawkins as she searches for answers only God can give.

Prologue

January, 1989

Lynnette had only been at the nursing home for twenty minutes when she wished she had taken her mother's advice to wait for her so they could visit Grandma Nelson together. Grandma Nelson was working on Lynnette's last nerve. At ninety-four, Delilah Mabel Colts-Nelson was old but very wise. Lynnette's mother Vivian would often rescue Lynnette from being preached to by Grandma Nelson. But today Lynnette was on her own.

Throughout Lynnette's entire childhood Grandma Nelson was her best friend, confidante, and Sunday school teacher. She had the answer to everything Lynnette ever wanted to know. When she was five-years old, Grandma Nelson gave her a t-shirt that read, "If Mom doesn't know, ask Grandma." Now at the age of twenty-two, Lynnette still found herself being lectured to by a woman whom she admired for her knowledge and wisdom.

"Baby, all I have to say is, don't never put no trust in no man, 'cause a man is man."

Lynnette folded her arms across her chest. "Dang, Grandma, you act like getting married is a sin or something."

Delilah lay in the bed and stared at her granddaughter for a moment, debating whether or not she should tell her that being married is not always fun and games. "Girl, let me tell you something. Your granddaddy was a good man in his own way. He worked hard every day, took care of his six kids, and all the while we was married, I never had to work. He made sure his family was taken care of."

Lynnette unfolded her arms and leaned on the table. "Yeah, and? Sounds to me like the perfect man."

"I ain't finished. When your momma was a little girl, she used to bring me the mail from the mailbox everyday. One day a letter came for your

1

granddaddy, and I opened it up and read it. When he got home and saw that the letter was opened, he asked me who opened up his mail. When I said it was me who opened the letter, you know what he did then? He slapped me cross my face so hard, felt like he set fire to it. He told me anything with his name on it is his business. He picked up the letter and looked at it for awhile then threw it on the table and told me to read it to him. Your granddaddy didn't have much schoolin' when he was a boy, so he couldn't read too good. Although he's been dead for twenty-five years, I just got word last year that he got another son the same age as your uncle Charlie."

Lynnette sat back in the chair. "Well that was the old days. Ain't no man gonna hit me in my face and get away with it. And as far as making babies here and there, that won't happen to me, 'cause I know for a fact that Gerald loves me. He tells me every day."

"Listen, Baby, Granny loves you too and I ain't never gonna tell you nothing that'll hurt you. But if you let a man control your life and give him all you got, that's in you, he'll hurt you real bad. I know what I'm talking about. I've seen it happen too many times."

Lynnette stood up and grabbed her purse and keys from the table. "Well like I said, Gerald loves me. I know he won't hurt me, and one day I'm gonna say 'I do' to the only man I ever loved and we're gonna live happily ever after. You just watch and see."

After she heard the door close, Grandma closed her eyes. "Lord, please watch over Lynnette. She don't know that her granddaddy told me he loved me too. But that love wasn't strong enough to keep him faithful."

Chapter 1

Lynnette could always tell by the ring of the telephone that it was Gerald calling. It had a romantic tone to it. Besides, it was one o'clock P.M. and Gerald always called on his lunch break. She answered the telephone with a sexy voice and a smile on her face. "Hello?"

"Hey, what's up?" This was his usual greeting.

Lynnette had just retrieved the mail from the mailbox, then she plopped down on the sofa in her one-bedroom apartment on Marengo Avenue in Westchester, a suburban community west of Chicago. "We got six more responses back today. So far the total is two hundred eighty-six people. Looks like Daddy is gonna have to cough up some more money to feed these folks at the reception. We only counted on two hundred fifty people showing up, but I guess a lot of people are looking forward to our big day just as much as we are. Can you believe it, Gerald? All these years we've been together, and in only three more weeks you and I will be married. Aren't you excited?"

"Uh, yeah, uh we need to talk. I gotta tell you something."

Her smile faded. "You sound sad. What's wrong?" she asked.

Gerald tensed up, but knew he had to tell her. "Do you remember when I suggested that we wait another year or two just to make sure all of our bills were paid off, and we were absolutely sure this is what we really wanted to do?"

"Yeah, I remember. But we talked about it and decided we can make it if we cut back on a lot of crazy spending."

"Do you remember telling me it's either now or never?" he asked.

Lynnette sighed and leaned back on the sofa. "Of course I remember, but why are you bringing this up? Are you having second thoughts again?"

Gerald glanced at his watch, hoping his lunch hour was over so he wouldn't have to get into this right now. What had already seemed like an hour had only been ten minutes. "It's a lot deeper than that. Something happened that you really need to know about."

The beads of sweat forming on her forehead, her shaking legs, and the tone of Gerald's voice told Lynnette that her fairytale love-life was about to come to an end. "What do you mean something happened?"

Knowing he couldn't stop there, he found the courage to continue. "There's someone else. You don't know her, but I've been spending some time with her."

Tears started to burn Lynnette's lower eyelids. She felt as though someone had sat on her chest and took her breath away. "Who is she, and how much time could you be spending with her? It can't be too much time, cause you and I are always together."

"I met Melanie two months ago in Bible class and we started talking and getting to know each other."

Lynnette stood up and put her left hand on her hip. "What are you telling me, Gerald? Are you saying that you want to call off the wedding?"

Gerald was quiet for at least ten seconds. "There's something else you should know." After another long pause, "We slept together."

The living room turned black. Nothing could be seen or heard. Lynnette dropped the telephone and fell to her knees. "Oh my God. No, not you, Gerald. How could you do this to me?"

Gerald heard Lynnette's telephone hit the floor and heard her screams.

"Lynnette, Lynnette, pick up the phone. Lynnette, please, we can talk about this. Lynnette, pick up the phone."

All of a sudden she was silent. She couldn't move. She wanted to die. At that moment life wasn't worth living. She heard him calling her name and picked up the telephone. "You told me you loved me. You said you'd never hurt me. I gave you all my love and you promised to take care of me."

"Baby, I do love you. Don't ever doubt that. It's just that I felt you were forcing me into this. I knew your parents had spent a lot of money, the invitations had gone out already, and I knew you had your dress. I was feeling pressured and Melanie was there for me to talk to. One thing led to another and it just happened."

"Don't give me that crap, Gerald. You and I both know that sex doesn't just happen. There is a lot more to it than that."

"I'm not about to tell you all the details, Lynnette, and you might as well know this too before you hear it from someone else."

She couldn't take anymore, but she had to know. "Wait, let me guess. She's pregnant, right? Gerald, please don't tell me she's pregnant."

"No, she's not pregnant. You need to know that two weeks ago when I told you that I needed your car to get to work, I lied. I borrowed your car so that she and I could spend the day together."

Lynnette felt like she was in the twilight zone. She couldn't believe it. She wouldn't believe it. This had to be a bad dream. She closed her eyes. *Lord, please wake me up from this nightmare.*

"Hello, Lynnette, are you there?"

"Gerald, you had the nerve to take my car and ride around with her having fun? Where was her car?"

"Her car wasn't running either, so I asked if I could borrow yours. I want you to know the reason I'm telling you this is because I do love you and I want us to get married. It was just a one-time thing. It didn't mean anything to me. Baby, I know we can work this out."

Lynnette hung up the telephone.

Chapter 2

Lynnette woke up the next day with her hair matted down, showing no sign of the relaxer she used two days before. Her heavy and swollen eyelids looked like two ping pong balls in the bathroom mirror. *Am I still wearing these clothes from yesterday?*

And then she remembered yesterday. *Why did yesterday have to happen?*

She left the bathroom and walked down the hall to the kitchen and looked at the refrigerator. *I ain't hungry. Nothing in there can make yesterday go away.*

She sat at the kitchen table and lowered her head. "Lord, what am I going to do now? My parents are going to have a fit. They've spent so much money on this wedding. There's no way I can tell them about this."

Then she thought, *I might as well get it over with, 'cause there ain't gonna be a wedding.* She got up from the table and dragged her feet, which felt like twenty-pound weights, across the floor to get to the telephone on the wall. *Lord, please don't let them be home.*

"Hello?"

"Hey, Mommie, whatcha doing?" She was trying to keep a steady voice, but the tears were starting to burn.

"Your father and I are on our way to put some flowers on your grandmother's grave. You wanna come with us?"

Good ole Grandma Nelson. If she was here today, I'd kiss her feet. If I had listened to her, I wouldn't be going through this mess.

"No, I just called to talk to you, that's all." *I can't do it. I can't tell them. Not now.*

"I'll call you when we get back from the cemetery. Oh, I forgot to tell you that the shoes you ordered from the Saks Fifth Avenue store came in

6

today. The store left a message on my machine this morning. It said you can pick them up in the catalog department."

Oh God, help me through this please. It wasn't enough that Lynnette's eyelids were burning but now her nose was starting to run, and no matter how hard she tried, she couldn't hold it in. "*Sniff, sniff.*"

"Lynnette, what's wrong, are you sick?"

I better get a grip, cause she can read me like a book. "No, it's just my sinuses acting up again, I'll be alright. Mommie, I've changed my mind about the shoes. Maybe we should look around some more."

"Look around some more? Girl, I paid one hundred eighty dollars for those shoes. You better get your butt over to that store and pick them up. Do you think money grows on trees?"

"No, Mommie, I just think it's too much money for shoes I'll never wear again. *Sniff, sniff.*"

"Why is it too much all of a sudden? Last month you were hollering about how you just had to have those particular shoes. Once you saw them you wouldn't even look at another shoe. Do you remember the scene you caused in the middle of the store? You said you'd die if I didn't get them for you."

Oh, mommie, if you only knew I died yesterday. "What time does the store close, Mommie? *Sniff, sniff.*"

"It closes at six o'clock. And when you get them, bring them over here, and put them in the closet with the dress. I don't want Gerald to accidentally see them. Okay?"

"*Sniff, sniff.* Yeah, okay, Mommie."

"And Lynnette, do something about that sinus problem. We can't have you sniffing like that on your wedding day."

"*Sniff, sniff.* I will, Mommie. I'll talk to you later and kiss Daddy for me. *Sniff, sniff.*"

Chapter 3

Lynnette knew that before she went anywhere, she should talk to Gerald, but she didn't want to call him. She went into the bathroom and started the water for a hot bath. She reached for the strawberry bath oil, but stopped when she remembered that Gerald bought it for her because she loves strawberries so much. She chose to use bath beads instead. She lay comfortably in the tub and let out a loud sigh. "Lord, what am I going to do? He told me he loved me."

"HE DOESN'T LOVE YOU."

Lynnette sat straight up in the tub. She noticed chill bumps on her arms. She looked around the bathroom expecting to see someone, but no one was there. She lay back in the tub. *I know I heard something.*

She soaked for another ten minutes, then drained the tub.

Getting dressed didn't go well for Lynnette. She managed to get as far as her socks, but she couldn't put her shoes on. She lay down on the bed. Her eyes started to burn, then the tears fell. She felt like there was nothing to live for. "Oh God, help me please. It hurts so bad and I don't know what to do. Please make this better for me."

"TRUST ME WHEN I TELL YOU THAT HE DOESN'T LOVE YOU. DO NOT GET MARRIED. HE'S NOT THE MATE THAT I HAVE CHOSEN FOR YOU. I WILL ALWAYS BE HERE FOR YOU BUT YOU'VE GOT TO TRUST ME."

Lynnette lay very still. She was afraid to move, even afraid to breathe. *Now I'm hearing voices. I must be losing my mind.*

The loud ring of the telephone startled her. She reached for the telephone on her nightstand. "Hello?"

"Hey, how are you?"

She sat up on the bed. *I know this fool ain't calling me.*

"How do you think I'm doing? Do you really care?"

"I wouldn't be calling to ask if I didn't care. Can we get together and talk?"

"Let me tell you something, Gerald Hawkins. You've got a lot of nerve calling me trying to talk about anything after what you've put me through. Exactly what do you want to talk about? You got something else you want to tell me about your girlfriend?"

"She's not my girlfriend. I don't even care about her. It was just a one-time thing. You are the one I love. Can I please come over so we can talk? I want to make things right between us."

I must be crazy for even considering this. "Yeah, you can come over."

She could hear the excitement in his voice. "Thanks, Baby, I'm on my way."

Lynnette hung up the telephone and sat there thinking, *No matter what he says, don't take him back, because if he did it once he'll do it again.*

She went into the bathroom to wash her face, brush her teeth, and pull her hair back into a ponytail. She applied some lipstick. *He ain't worth the lipstick.* Then she sprayed on a little perfume. *I might as well smell good too.*

Gerald arrived in less than fifteen minutes. *What did he do, call from around the corner?*

She opened the door and the vision before her eyes took her breath away. His head and face were clean shaven. He had flowers and candy in his hands. *No matter what he says.*

She stepped aside, and he came in and stood very close to her, close enough for her to smell his Drakkar cologne. Gerald knew that one whiff of Drakkar cologne mesmerized Lynnette.

"These are for you."

She wanted to take the gifts he bought for her, but she knew he was trying to break her down. "This is not a rendezvous. You said you wanted to talk."

He revealed a pint of strawberries that were hidden behind his back. *Now he's playing dirty, but no matter what he says or does, he won't break me.*

"I don't want those either, and if you're not here to talk, you can leave."

He walked into the kitchen and put the gifts on the counter, then sat down at the table. She followed and sat across from him.

"Come and sit on my lap."

"I'm fine right here."

"You look good, Baby, smell good too."

No matter what he says. "What do you want to talk about, Gerald?"

"I can see you're not going to make this easy for me, are you?" he said.

Lynnette wanted to strangle him. "Why should I make anything easy for you? You certainly haven't made things easy for me."

9

Gerald reached across the table to grab her hands, but she pulled them away. "Baby, I'm so sorry, I really am. I know I've messed things up, but I love you and I want us to get married."

No matter what he says. "Three weeks ago you had an affair and now you want to get married? I'm sorry, but I can't accept this."

"Lynnette, please forgive me. I promise to spend the rest of my life making this up to you. I don't want to lose you. You are my world, my everything. I can't imagine my life without you. Please say you'll marry me, Baby, please."

No matter what he says. "What about your girlfriend?"

"Stop calling her my girlfriend. She's not my girlfriend. I've already told her I made a mistake with her and that my heart is with you."

"And what did she say?"

"It doesn't matter what she said. I'm here with you, aren't I?"

No matter what he says, be strong. "I don't know, Gerald. How can I ever trust you again?"

He got up from the table, came over to Lynnette, got down on one knee in front of her, and grabbed her hands. "I promise you I will do whatever it takes for you to trust me again. I love you, Lynnette. Don't leave me. Please, I'm begging you, Baby, don't leave me."

I know I shouldn't believe him, but are those tears in his eyes? Maybe he really is sorry.

"I forgive you, Gerald. Of course I'll marry you, but you're gonna have to take an AIDS test."

"I was careful. You don't have to worry about that."

"I don't care. This is my body. Either you take the test or we don't get married."

Gerald stood up and pulled her into his arms. "Okay, I'll take the test and you won't regret this. I'm going to love you forever."

It feels so good to be in his arms again. Lynnette glanced at the clock which read five fifteen P.M. and remembered her wedding shoes. "I've got to be somewhere before six o'clock."

"Come on, I'll take you," Gerald said.

"No, that's okay. I need to do this by myself."

"Can I stay here until you get back?"

Lynnette was hoping he'd ask. "Sure, I'd like that."

She went into the bedroom to put on her shoes. When she returned to the kitchen she noticed that Gerald had washed the strawberries and was putting her flowers in water. After she placed a juicy kiss on his lips, she left for the mall. "I knew he loved me." She said to herself when she got in the car.

"HE DOESN'T LOVE YOU."
Lynnette froze. *Why am I hearing voices?*
She shook off the shivers and drove away.

Believing that Holy Matrimony is ordained by God
and in the spirit of Christian joy
Mr. and Mrs. Walter and Vivian Nelson
request the honor of your presence
at the wedding ceremony of their daughter

Lynnette Diane Nelson
and
Gerald Michael Hawkins

son of Mr. and Mrs. David and Thelma Hawkins
on Saturday, June 23rd, 1992
at three o' clock in the afternoon
Mount Vernon Baptist Church
4514 Jefferson Drive
Richton Park, Il

It was standard procedure for Lynnette to get her hair done every Saturday morning at nine o'clock. No matter what else she had to do, getting her hair done was mandatory and had first priority.

"Well, look who's here. It's the newlywed herself."

"Hey, Janice. Did you miss me?"

Janice, her longtime friend and beautician, greeted her with a hug. "Not really. You only missed a week. From the look of things I can tell you gave your pillow much use. Girl your head looks like ten-year-old carpet. What did you do on your honeymoon, fight in a war?"

Lynnette laughed as she sat down in the familiar chair. "You know how it is when you're a newlywed. Some things just can't be helped. Oops, I'm sorry. You don't know, do you?"

Janice took a step back from Lynnette and put her hand on her hip. "I know you ain't trying to get sassy. Just because you got a man that's finer than fine and he *is* fine, I'm just gonna put the truth on out there. That don't mean you're all that."

"Honey, I'm all that *and* a bag of chips, and some Cheetos, plus some Doritos and don't you forget it. Now come on and hook me up. I ain't trying to be in here all day messing with you. I have places to go and people to see."

"You ain't foolin nobody, Lynnette. You're just trying to get out of here so you can run up behind Gerald."

"If I wanted to run up behind the Pope, that would be my business and not yours. Now hook me up."

Janice placed a towel on Lynnette's shoulders. "I got a new style for you today, and I don't want to see you at church tomorrow looking like a peacock.

So tell that husband of yours to take it easy. I can't have my specialty looking like you did it yourself."

Lynnette looked up at Janice. "Are you saying I can't do my own hair?"

"Obviously you can't or you wouldn't be coming to me every week."

Lynnette leaned back into the sink. "Ain't nothing wrong with the truth. By the way, I'm going to Gerald's church tomorrow. This will be the first time I've gone there."

Janice stopped shampooing her hair. "Is this going to be a permanent thing? Are you thinking of moving your membership?"

She didn't want Janice to know the real reason she was looking forward to going to Gerald's church. She wanted to get a good look at this Melanie person. "In our last counseling session Pastor Graham told us husbands and wives should worship together. He said being together in the presence of God will strengthen our marriage, and he's already given me my letter of transfer."

Janice rinsed out Lynnette's hair and sat her in the styling chair for her roller set. "Well we will miss you over at Mount Vernon, so don't become a stranger."

"Mount Vernon will always be my home. I'll be popping up over there every now and then, and you and I will never lose touch because I'll still be here every Saturday morning as usual."

The door opened and Evangelist Debra Thomas walked in. Just like Lynnette, she had a standard appointment every Saturday morning. She would show up at Janice's House of Hair Beauty Salon at nine thirty A.M. come rain or shine. Debra, also a member of Mount Vernon, has been a friend of Lynnette's since they first met in church. She, Janice, and Lynnette have been singing in the choir together for the past five years.

"Good morning, ladies." Debra was always in a good mood, no matter what. Even on her worst days she would smile as if nothing bothered her. She had no problem letting whoever crossed her path know that she served a living God.

One Saturday morning, the salon was crowded because Janice was going on vacation the next week. Although there were four other beauticians working for Janice, she closed the shop when she went out of town, because according to her, no one else was trustworthy enough to keep things under control in her absence. Therefore, both the weekday and the weekend customers were packed in the salon like sardines. When Debra walked in, she said her good mornings, sat down, and waited her turn. To her left, three women shared in a conversation about how good their sexual experiences were. Debra noticed that none of the women wore wedding bands. To her right, one lady told another how she was going to cuss somebody out when she got home. Sitting across from Debra was a young girl, who appeared to be no more that sixteen-years-old, reading a Playgirl magazine. Debra felt like she was sitting in the audience of one of those trashy talk shows, so she got up and asked Janice for the keys to her office. Janice gave her the keys thinking that she wanted to use the telephone. When Debra got back to her seat, she got her Bible out of her bag and started to read. Every customer was quiet and all eyes were on her.

When she was in Janice's office, she had turned on the radio and blasted the gospel station over the intercom. For the next ten minutes, no one said a word. The beauticians were working quietly, and Debra kept reading her Bible. By the time her name was called, the entire atmosphere had changed. Ladies went from gossiping and planning to cuss somebody out, to singing and patting their feet.

Today Debra spoke first. "Good morning."

Janice said, "Hey there. Come on in and have a seat. I'll be with you as soon as I get Lynnette under the dryer."

"Take your time. I ain't in no hurry. Lynnette, I have to say that you were one beautiful bride. And that dress, Girl, you looked like the perfect angel. That was a good idea you had to sing to Gerald. Those words of love and commitment almost made me cut a step. God has blessed you with a beautiful voice and I want you to promise me that whatever happens in your life you will keep singing to the glory of God, because He's worthy."

"Okay, Debra, I promise." *She always makes me feel good, but what does she mean no matter what happens? What could happen?*

"And speaking of singing, why weren't you at choir rehearsal last night?" asked Debra.

Janice is known for speaking when she's not spoken to. "Because Girlfriend was honeymooning last night. Ain't that right, Sister girl?"

"No, that ain't right, and she wasn't even talking to you, Miss Thang. But to answer your question, Debra, I didn't come because I've been thinking of joining Gerald's church, New Friendship Baptist over on Halsted Lane."

Debra leaned forward and grabbed Lynnette's hands. "That's a wonderful thing. A family that prays together, stays together. Always keep God in the center of your marriage and everything will be alright."

"Okay, Lynnette, you're ready for the dryer and make sure you stay under there a whole hour this time. I don't know why black folks don't like the dryer. Some of them are going to end up someplace hotter than a dryer."

"You would know wouldn't you, Janice? When you get there, tell all your friends I said hey."

"You better be careful, Lynnette, because I may just meet you down there."

"I don't think so, Honey. My seat is already reserved on the right hand of the Father. It's got my name on it."

"Oh yeah? Well right now your name is on the seat under this hot dryer. Come on, Debra, let me wash you and get you under there too. I've got a circle weave coming in here in ten minutes."

14

The radio alarm woke her up at eight thirty A.M. Wrapped in Gerald's arms, Lynnette wished they could stay that way forever. She started to wake Gerald in order to allow him first use of the bathroom, because she needed to lie there and prepare herself for Miss Melanie. Suddenly the words from the radio caused her to lie still and listen. ***"Whatever comes my way, whatever path I'm destined to walk, just keep Your arms around me. Hold me tight, Lord, and don't let go. When the dark clouds begin to cry, keep Your loving arms around me."***

When the song ended, Lynnette turned off the alarm. She lay there thinking to herself about how appropriate that song was for today. She didn't know what was ahead of her, but she did know she wanted the Lord to keep His loving arms around her.

"I LOVE YOU AND I'M HOLDING YOU."

A cold shiver ran down her back and shook her. The shiver caused Gerald to stir, and Lynnette turned over to face him. "Good morning, Honey."

Gerald took a long stretch. "Good morning." He saw the chill bumps and ran his hand over her arm. "Why are you so cold?"

She snuggled up next to him. "I don't know. Lately I've been having chills."

"Maybe a nice hot shower with me will warm you up."

"I don't think we should shower together if you want to be on time for morning service at ten o' clock."

Gerald got out of bed and walked to the bathroom. "Suit yourself."

Lynnette looked at his long, lean body. "Well maybe a short hot shower wouldn't be too bad."

15

What was supposed to be a short hot shower turned into a long hot shower, so they were late for morning service anyway. After the Usher had seated them and gave them their programs, Lynnette leaned over to Gerald. "Where is she?"

Gerald looked at her. "Where is who?"

Now he's got amnesia. "Melanie, that's who."

"Why do you wanna know?"

Lynnette turned her whole body to face him and gave him the famous neck movement women give when they're really trying to make a point. "Because I wanna know. Have you got a problem with that?"

"I don't want you starting trouble, Lynnette. You know how you are."

She increased the neck movement. "No, I don't know, Gerald. How am I?"

"Like that."

"What are you talking about? Like what?"

A lady sitting on the pew in front of them turned and glanced at them both.

Gerald lowered his voice. "Can we please talk about this later? We are in church."

"Yeah, you can count on it." Lynnette turned her attention to the pulpit.

"We will now have a solo by Sister Melanie Williams," the program director said.

The music started, and Lynnette's heart began beating so fast she could see it pumping through her blouse. A young lady stood in the choir stand and the program director gave her a microphone. She was beautiful, light-skinned, had long hair, and could really blow. Lynnette didn't want to admit it, but she knew the sister could sing. *Hmph, she don't sound better than me. I bet I could give her a run for her money.*

Lynnette couldn't take her eyes off of her. *She weighs about fifty pounds less than I do.*

She glanced over at Gerald, who was sweating bullets. His face looked like he used Vaseline instead of lotion.

"What's wrong with you?"

Gerald knew he had to get out of there quick, fast and in a hurry because Lynnette was getting upset. "It's hot in here. I'm going to get a drink of water."

He said it was over between them. He's acting mighty funny for something to be over. If it was really over, she wouldn't affect him like this.

Gerald stayed outside for the rest of the service. When Pastor Jones gave the benediction, Lynnette was the first one out of the sanctuary. Outside, Gerald sat on the church steps. Lynnette didn't say a word and walked right by him. He caught up with her just as she got to his truck and opened the door for her. When he got behind the wheel, he looked at her.

"Are you okay?" he asked.

She didn't look at him and kept her head straight. "Uh huh."

Gerald started the engine and pulled away from the curb. He always knew when she was angry. This was definitely one of those times when if there was going to be any conversation, he would have to do all of the talking.

"Where do you want to go for dinner?" he asked.

She continued to look straight ahead. "Don't worry about me. Take me home, then you can go and get something if you want to."

When Gerald pulled into the driveway, he put the gear in park and looked at her. "Are you sure you don't want anything to eat?"

"Yep."

"Are you going to cook something?"

"Nope," she said.

Whenever they enter the house together, Gerald always insists on opening the door for her. But not this time. She had her own key out and ready for entry.

"Let me get that for you," he said. Before he could finish his sentence, she was already in the living room.

He walked in behind her. "Is there something you wanna talk about?"

She remained silent. He watched as she kicked off her heels and threw her purse on the cocktail table.

"Lynnette, what's wrong?"

She wouldn't look at him. *You figure it out.* She walked into the bedroom and fell across the bed. He started to follow her but then decided against it. Deep down inside, Gerald knew what was wrong. What he didn't know was how to fix it. Frustrated and hungry, he left the house. Lynnette lay in bed and cried. "Why did I get myself into this? Lord, please help me."

"YOU DIDN'T TRUST ME BUT I'M STILL HOLDING YOU."

She felt the shivers again, so she pulled the sheets over her legs. *I'll make a doctor's appointment in the morning. Maybe I'm coming down with the flu.*

It was after midnight when Gerald got home. In the bedroom, Lynnette was asleep. He undressed and got into bed. When he moved next to her, he saw that she had on a quilted gown that covered her from neck to toe. He assumed she put it on because of the chills, but the truth was Lynnette wanted to send him a message that said, "**hands off, not tonight, or don't even think about it.**"

She didn't care which one he chose, as long as he got the message. When she woke up the next morning Gerald had already left for work.

Only You

You are unique, dear woman. That is what makes you priceless. The Lord will never, ever replace you. Though He has millions more children, each one wonderful, none is exactly like you! Never give up your uniqueness in order to be what you admire in someone else. Glean all you can from everyone, but duplicate none. You are too priceless as an original to be reduced to a cheap copy!

Perhaps you don't understand what an amazing jewel of a woman you are. The Lord created you for a purpose that only you can fulfill. Have you yet realized how intensely God loves you? In spite of your afflictions, He loves you. The Father sweeps you up into His arms and clutches you. He holds your head to His breast, your ear to His heart. He has held you through rough places, trusting the strength of His arms to keep you through the pains of life.

Before you feel unloved, take a moment and think. Isn't there evidence in your life that, from time to time, He has brought you through a storm? Don't you dare act as if the Father doesn't love you just because He doesn't cater to you. Perhaps you should be glad for the love He has already shown and the night rides He has already carried you through. That love constantly affirms your uniqueness.

If God hadn't made you as He did, you wouldn't have been able to persevere as you have. There are many people who couldn't take what you have been through. God wants to use you in a unique way to be a blessing to those around you. Remember, people are blessed when you are sincere-not perfect.

Don't let anyone manipulate you into forsaking your own uniqueness. Those people weren't built for your life's destiny, and they can't play your role. Aren't you glad that God prepared you for life instead of preparing life for you? So, whether life is ready for you or not, you are ready for it! Just tell the world, "Get ready, get ready, get ready!"

Chapter 6

To Lynnette, it seemed like it was just yesterday when she started working at Loyola University Medical Center in Maywood. When she accepted the position as "Hospice Coordinator" in charge of assigning nurses to care for cancer patients on a daily basis, she thought it would be too depressing. But working ten hour days in a smokeless environment in order to have a three-day weekend, plus having the privilege of listening to her gospel CDs throughout the day, made it easy to come to work. Every day for the past five and a half years, she got to work on time and made sure that her patients received the best care possible. This was one place where Lynnette knew she was reaching out to help someone else in need. She wouldn't leave the office until she had called each patient's home to inquire about the nurse's treatment toward the patient. One thing Lynnette was thankful for was she had the authority to interview and pick which nurse to send and care for each patient. Some of the qualities she looked for in a nurse were patience, tenderness, loving kindness, and most importantly, all nurses had to be saved. Lynnette made it standard procedure that each nurse end their visit with the patient in prayer. She even required a letter from each of the nurse's Pastors stating that he or she was in good standing with their church. Whenever Lynnette would get a report that a patient was near the end, she would accompany the nurse on one of the visits and pray with the patient herself. Often when a patient had passed on, Lynnette received a letter from the family thanking her for her time, dedication, and thoughtfulness. During Lynnette's third year of employment, her supervisor Betty Jenkins called Lynnette into her office and presented her with a hefty raise. Betty told Lynnette she had been getting great comments and admiration for a job well done. She graciously thanked Betty for the raise and said, "It's not me, but it's the Jesus in me."

Lynnette could recall six times when other departments in the medical center tried to recruit her to join them by waving a nice dollar sign in her face. She would tell Betty, and each time Betty would offer an even nicer dollar sign to keep Lynnette in her department. When Lynnette told Evangelist Debra Thomas about the raises, she would say to Lynnette, "See what paying your tithes and offerings gets you?" Lynnette was living proof that the more you give, the more God gives to you. She made a habit of always paying her tithes and offerings before she paid anything else. This way she knew she would never be without any money.

The normal time for Lynnette to begin work was eight o'clock A.M. However, she made a strong effort to be at work no later than seven thirty A.M. She allowed herself thirty minutes before start time for meditation and scripture reading. She found that if she didn't come into the presence of God before work, that day would definitely have its downs.

This particular morning, Lynnette had more on her mind than scripture reading, meditation, and her patients. She couldn't understand why Gerald behaved the way he did in church yesterday. When she got to her desk, she saw the light on her telephone flashing, indicating she had at least one message. She put her things away in the bottom drawer and pressed the button. "You have twenty-three messages. To listen, press one." Lynnette sat down and took notes as she cleaned out her voice mailbox.

Nurse Yolanda reported that one of her patients had developed pneumonia. Nurse Gayle reported that one of her patients refused medication, and Nurse Jocelyn reported that the insurance company of one of her patients had terminated his policy. The last message was from this morning. It was Lynnette's mother welcoming her back to work.

I'll call you later, Mommie.

Lynnette got up and went into the file room to pull files on the patients on whom she took notes. Upon leaving the file room, she bumped into Betty.

"Oh, excuse me, Betty. I wasn't looking where I was going."

"That's okay, Lynnette, welcome back."

"Thank you. It's good to be back. How are things around here?"

Betty put the back of her hand on her forehead as though she was going to faint. "Girl, look, the next time you decide to take a whole month off, make sure you take your patients with you, because they wore me out. I'm getting too old for this. Mrs. Blythe wouldn't open the door and let the nurse in one morning. She said she was tired of getting poked with needles every day. Mrs. Taylor said it's against her religion to swallow aspirin, and Mr. Perez said his male nurse is too mean, so he has requested a female nurse instead. He had the nerve to tell me to send him a young one. As old as that man is, can you believe that?"

Lynnette had to laugh at that. "Yep, that's Mr. Perez alright. As picky as he is, I bet he outlives you and me. He refuses to let his colon cancer get the best of him."

Betty turned and started toward the cafeteria. "Well, I'm glad you're back. These patients made me age ten years. Now I'm gonna have to hire a nurse to come to my house and take care of me. Make sure you send me a male nurse, a good-looking young one."

"Betty, you are a trip. I don't know who's worse, you or Mr. Perez." Lynnette took the files back to her desk and saw the light on her telephone blinking again. "I guess there's no rest for the weary today, huh Lord?"

She pressed the button and heard Gerald's voice. "Hey, how are you? I just called to see if you got to work okay. I have a busy day, but I'll try to call you back on my lunch break. I love you, and I miss you."

Normally whenever she heard his voice she'd smile, but today it didn't move her at all.

By the end of the day, Lynnette had managed to call every patient, prepare the nurses' schedule for the next day, and clear her desk of all the paperwork from the month before. She glanced at the clock and saw that it was three twenty P.M. *Time sure flies when you're having fun.*

She leaned forward on the desk, and placed her face in her hands, wondering if she should apologize to Gerald. Maybe she overreacted yesterday. Gerald said it was over between him and Melanie. After all, she was the one wearing his wedding ring, not her. *Maybe I'm being too hard on him.*

She mumbled. "Lord, help me today."

"I'M HERE FOR YOU MY DAUGHTER."

Lynnette shivered in her chair and reached for her sweater. She didn't hear Betty walk up to her.

"So, how was your first day back?"

"Fine. I was so busy, I didn't realize it was so late."

"You were very quiet today. Are you okay?"

"Yeah, I just got a lot on my mind that's all." *Please don't ask me if I want to talk about it because I don't.*

"Well, if you need to talk, I'm here for you."

"Thanks, Betty, it's nothing major. I'll work it out."

She looked at Lynnette's sweater. "Can I ask you something?"

"Sure, what's up?"

"Why are you wearing a sweater when it's ninety degrees outside and seventy degrees in here?"

"I caught a chill. I've been having them a lot lately."

"You know I can't allow you to visit any of the patients if you think you're sick. We try to keep them as germ-free as possible."

"Yes, I know. I will definitely make a doctor's appointment in the morning. If you don't mind, I'm going to leave early today and go home to lie down."

Betty rubbed her shoulder. "Sure, Sweetie, go ahead and take care of yourself. I'll see you in the morning."

Lynnette turned off her desk lamp and hung up her sweater. "Thanks, Betty. Good night."

Chapter 7

On the way home from work, Lynnette passed a grocery store and it dawned on her that it had been almost three weeks since the wedding, and she had yet to cook her husband a decent meal. She wanted to go home and apologize to Gerald for giving him the cold shoulder yesterday, and thought a home-cooked meal may help soften things up. She made a U-turn and headed to the grocery store.

Fried pork chops, homemade macaroni and cheese, potato salad, and corn-on-the-cob was what she wanted to prepare for Gerald. She had about thirty dollars cash in her wallet, but she realized she also needed seasoned salt, flour, pepper, mustard, and vegetable oil. They hadn't gone grocery shopping yet, and she remembered the day she moved in with Gerald, his cabinets were bare. Lynnette hoped she had everything she needed, and wrote a check for over one hundred dollars.

Gerald's Chevrolet Blazer was in the driveway when she got home. *He's home early too. I wonder what's up.*

She parked her car next to his truck, unloaded the groceries, and went inside. When she opened the front door, there was an aroma coming from the kitchen. She walked in just as Gerald was removing a pan covered with aluminum foil from the oven.

She spoke first. "Hi."

"Hi. Whatcha got there?" Gerald asked.

"Just a few groceries. I wanted to surprise you with dinner, but I see the surprise is on me, huh?"

"Well, I really didn't like the way things were between us yesterday. So I thought a nice and quiet evening at home would help smooth things over. I wanted to do something special for you, so I made you dinner. Surprise."

He does love me, I knew he did. "Thank you, Honey. I had the same idea, so I stopped at the grocery store for a few things on my way home from work and while I was there, I realized we haven't had a chance to buy groceries, so I picked up a few *more* things and ended up spending over one hundred dollars."

"Guess what?" He had a funny look on his face.

"What?"

"I stopped at the grocery store on my way home from work too, and spent about seventy-five dollars."

They both laughed, then Lynnette said, "Well between the two of us, we shouldn't go hungry for two weeks."

"Come on now, the way you eat, I think we'll be shopping again in the next three days. By the way, why are you home so early?"

Did he say "the way I eat?" I had to have heard him wrong. I know he didn't say that.

"I caught the chills again and I just wanted to get out of there and come home to make up with you. Why are you home so early?"

"A bunch of us architects were at a job sight in the northern suburbs when it started to rain, and since it was close to quitting time, the boss told us to go on home. Plus, I wanted to come home and make up with you too."

Lynnette sat the bags down on the table, walked over to her husband, and kissed him on the lips. "I love you and don't ever forget it."

Gerald returned the kiss. "I love you and don't *you* ever forget it."

She turned her attention towards dinner. "Something smells good, what is it?"

Gerald put his hand over her eyes and guided her out of the kitchen. "It's a surprise. I want you to go and change into something more comfortable, and when you get back, dinner will be served."

"You are so sweet. Give me a few minutes."

When she got back to the kitchen, dinner was on the table just as he promised.

"Come, my Queen, and have a seat." He pulled her chair out for her, she sat down and looked at the dinner Gerald had prepared for her. On her plate was a very small baked chicken breast and three Brussels sprouts. She looked at Gerald's plate and saw two fried chicken legs and french fries. He saw the look in her eyes, and knew right away that she wanted to question him, so he quickly sat down. "I'm going to bless the food. Bow your head, please."

Lynnette did as he asked but was anxious for him to finish. She kept her eyes open throughout the entire prayer.

He was just about done. "In Jesus' name, Amen."

"Amen. What's this?"

"It's your dinner. I made it especially for you."

She looked at his plate, then looked at her plate. She looked at his plate again, then looked at her plate. "Why is my chicken baked and yours fried? And why do I have Brussels sprouts when you've got a plate full of curly fries?"

"I kinda sorta thought you might want to change your eating habits a little." He nervously picked up his glass and drank some juice.

Lynnette looked at her glass and saw ice water. "What the heck is going on? What do you mean you kinda sorta thought? Did I tell you I wanted to change what I eat? Why do I have water and you have grape juice?"

"Water will help cleanse your system," Gerald said.

Lord, You're gonna have to forgive me, because it's about to get ugly up in here.

Lynnette put her hands on her hips, and on came the neck movement. "Who are you, my doctor? Are you trying to put me on a diet?"

Gerald pushed his chair back from the table and crossed his legs. "All I'm trying to do is help you lose a little weight."

Lynnette stood up. "What's wrong with my weight? You've never had a problem with it before."

"Will you please calm down? You don't have to get upset. I would just really like it if you lost some weight. It's no big deal."

"Well it's a real big deal to me. I wanna know why my weight bothers you all of a sudden. You used to tell me how good I look. I am the same size now as I was when you proposed to me. You liked it then. So now what's the problem?"

Gerald stood up and grabbed her hands. "There is no problem. I just want you to be healthy. Don't you wanna be healthy?"

"I *am* healthy and I look good too."

"Yeah, you look good, but you could look better."

Lynnette stepped back from him. *No he didn't.*

"What did you say to me?"

"I said you can look better."

"Like who, Melanie?" Lynnette asked.

"Don't even go there. This ain't got nothing to do with Melanie. This is between you and me."

Lynnette looked at him for about five seconds. "Oh, now I know what this is about. You're trying to turn me into her. Well I ain't her. My name is Lynnette, and if you wanted to marry someone her size, then you should've married her, cause you aren't going to change me."

Gerald sat down in the chair. "Look, Lynnette, I'm going to be honest. I'm not satisfied with the way you look, and I really want you to do something about it. If you love me like you say you do, you'll go on a diet and lose some weight."

Lynnette couldn't believe what her husband was saying to her. "And what if I don't?"

He stood up again. "Either you lose some weight, or you lose me."

Gerald walked past her and out the front door. She went into the bedroom in tears and kneeled by the bed. "Lord, what is happening to my marriage?"

"I TOLD YOU THAT HE DIDN'T LOVE YOU. YOU DIDN'T TRUST ME BUT I'M STILL HOLDING YOU."

That night, Lynnette cried herself to sleep. The next morning, the alarm clock woke her up at six o' clock. After she turned off the alarm, she glanced over her shoulder and saw that Gerald's side of the bed had not been slept on.

Beautiful Package, Beautiful Gift

The greatest part of your attractiveness-the part that draws or attracts other people to you-is on the inside, not on your flesh. Our society spends billions of dollars a year to convince you to buy hundreds, even thousands of dollars worth of clothes and makeup in order to fix up something that doesn't really matter all that much. We spend countless hours at beauty salons and spas and malls in order to buy, acquire, or create the things we think will draw other people to us, but which actually have very little drawing power. What you create or design on the outside of yourself may turn a head or two, but it is powerless to turn a mind or a heart.

You are bombarded daily with messages that tell you that if you will only go to the right weight-loss center and get down to the right size, dye your hair the right shade, go to the right spa, use the right toothpaste, put on the right makeup, wear the right outfit at the right time, and be seen in the right places with the right people, then you will most certainly be able to attract the right man and have the right children and live in the right neighborhood and enjoy the right kind of life!

When we do this and nothing "right" happens for us, we are puzzled. We sit back and ask, "What went wrong?" This is what went wrong. We became the merchandise for those who tried to sell us the merchandise. We've been had! The average woman, Christians included, will spend thousands of dollars this year on hats and hair color, earrings and evening dresses. Sadly, they will make no real investment to build up or support those inner qualities that truly attract others to us and to Jesus Christ our Savior.

If you are only concerned with what you look like, you are going to be a very shallow, superficial person. People are going to find that once they have quit playing with you, the box you came in was beautifully wrapped, but empty.

Go back to the source of your attractiveness-the Holy Spirit of God. He is the One who woos and wins the heart. When you are His woman, He will draw you to the right people for the right purposes at just the right time.

Chapter 8

If anyone among you thinks he is religious, and does not bridle his tongue but deceives his own heart, this one's religion is useless. James 1:26

It wasn't until Friday evening when Gerald finally came home. Lynnette was in the kitchen placing the dinner she cooked into plastic containers. Although Gerald heard her moving around in the kitchen, he went directly to the bedroom. Lynnette sat the containers on top of the stove and went into the bedroom behind him. He was emptying his duffel bag into the dirty clothes hamper. He sensed her presence and glanced toward the doorway. "Hey."

She walked in and leaned on the dresser. "Hey."

"Is there any mail for me?" he asked.

He doesn't come home for four days and he forgets his routine. I should tell him that there isn't any.

"It's on your desk where it always is."

The tone of her voice caused him to stop what he was doing and look at her. "What's up with the attitude?"

"I wanna know why you had to ask if there's any mail. Any other time you'd go right to your desk to see for yourself. Did you change your address? Were you not expecting any mail to come here anymore?"

Gerald threw the empty duffel bag on the bed then stood in front of her. "What's that supposed to mean?"

"They are simple questions, Gerald. Did you change your address? Are you still paying the mortgage on this house? Where have you been laying your head this week?"

Gerald walked away from her, went into the bathroom, and turned on the water in the shower. He didn't answer any of her questions.

While Gerald was in the shower, Lynnette took the opportunity to talk to God. She sat down at the kitchen table, put her elbows on the table, and placed her head in her hands. "My God, I'm seeking Your direction in this marriage. I truly love my husband, but I'm beginning to feel as though he doesn't love me. I need You to tell me what to do."

She sat there for a few minutes wondering what she could do to make things right again. Gerald came into the kitchen, walked to the stove, and looked inside the containers to see what she cooked. He put the lids back on the containers, got a glass from the cabinet, and filled it with water from the sink. Lynnette had to do something to break the ice.

"How was your shower?"

He turned toward her and leaned against the sink. "It was a shower, nothing to shout about."

Okay, let's try something else. "Do you want something to eat?"

He finished his water then folded his arms across his chest. "Why did you make meatloaf and mashed potatoes?"

"What do you mean, why did I make it? I made it because I had a taste for it."

"Couldn't you just settle for a small salad?" Gerald asked.

Couldn't you just get your teeth fixed? She couldn't believe that he was starting this mess again.

"I didn't want a salad, Gerald. What is your problem?"

"I told you that if you really wanted this marriage you would lose some weight."

Lynnette got up and walked over to him. "I am a twenty-five-year-old woman, and I will not allow you to treat me like a child who you can tell what and what not to eat. It's obvious you've got a problem, and I don't know what it is, but I do know it's not me. I am not grossly overweight or a sloppy person. As a matter of fact, when I look in the mirror, I see a beautiful black woman, a woman who any real man would be proud to have as his wife. So if you're looking for a reason to get out of this marriage, you're gonna have to come up with something other than my weight. I won't let you use me as your scapegoat."

She then grabbed a plate from the dish rack, topped it with meatloaf, mashed potatoes, and gravy, and got herself a glass of chocolate milk. Then she sat down at the table, said Grace, and started to eat. Gerald got himself another glass of water, then went into the living room, turned on the television, and lay on the couch.

After dinner Lynnette washed her dishes then went into the living room. "I'm going to put the food away. Do you want me to make you a plate?"

Gerald didn't take his eyes off the television. She stood there, watched him for a moment, then went back into the kitchen, and put the food in the refrigerator.

She went into the bathroom and ran herself some bath water. Just as she lay back in the tub, she heard Gerald's pager beep. She heard him go into the bedroom, close the door, and make a phone call. She shut her eyes, lay very still and tried to listen to what he said, but couldn't hear anything through the two doors. She washed her body quickly, then got out of the tub, and dried off. When she opened the door to the bedroom, Gerald was fully dressed. His overstuffed duffel bag was on the bed.

"Where are you going?"

Gerald was tying his shoes. "I'm going to stay with a friend until I figure out what to do about us."

"So you're just gonna pack up and leave? What about your wedding vows?"

"It's in the Bible that if a man is unhappy in his home, he should separate himself from whatever is making him unhappy."

This fool is crazy.

"What? Are you saying God told you to leave me? Where is that written, Gerald? What book and what chapter? I want you to find it for me before you leave."

He grabbed his duffel bag. "I don't know exactly where it's at, but it's in there."

Lynnette followed him to the front door. "Is it in the Old or New Testament?"

"I'll show it to you when I find it."

"Who paged you?"

"None of your business. Do I ask who's calling you all the time?"

He opened the door and walked out, and Lynnette followed him onto the porch. "When are you coming back?"

Gerald kept on walking. "When I feel like it, maybe never."

Tears filled her eyes. "I love you, Gerald."

When he opened the door to his truck, he turned to look at her. "Prove it."

He got in the Chevrolet Blazer, backed out of the driveway, and drove down the street.

Lynnette walked back into the house, turned off the television, turned off all the lights, went into the bedroom, and got on her knees. "Lord, I've lost my husband. What am I going to do now?"

"WASH, IRON AND FOLD HIS CLOTHES."

She cried. She didn't understand God at that particular moment, but she did as she was told.

Chapter 9

"Hey, Lynnette."

"Hi, Janice, how are you?"

"I'm even more blessed today than I was yesterday. How are you?"

Lynnette sat down in the wash chair. "I'm blessed too."

She didn't sound very convincing and Janice being as nosy as she is picked up on it. "Well you sure don't sound like it. Are you alright?"

Lynnette really needed to talk to somebody, but Janice was the wrong somebody. Her mouth was like an Energizer battery. It just keeps on going and going and going. If you ever wanted the whole world to know about your business, all you had to do was tell it to Janice, and she was guaranteed to put it in the Extra Newspaper so everyone could read all about it. Lynnette knew she couldn't trust Janice with her personal life. "Yeah, I'm fine. I just got a little upset stomach."

Janice gave her a slight smile.

"What are you smiling at?"

She leaned Lynnette back into the wash bowl. "Nothing. I'll wait until you're ready to tell me."

"Ready to tell you what?"

Janice kept on shampooing. "Whatever it is you've got to tell me." She towel dried Lynnette's hair and sat her down in the styling chair. "So whenever you're ready just come right out and say it."

Lynnette looked in the mirror at Janice. She was standing behind her, clipping her ends. "You must be on that stuff, cause I don't have a clue what you're talkin' about, and I don't think you do either."

Janice stopped clipping and looked at Lynnette in the mirror. "Go ahead and play dumb, but you know you can't hide it forever."

"Girl, how much of that stuff are you sniffing? You need to stop, because it's got you talking crazy."

"You are the crazy one if you think you can keep something like this from me. You know that I know everything about everybody, so you might as well come on out with it."

Lynnette was losing patience. "Okay, you are giving me a headache, so this conversation is over. Hurry up and get me under the dryer so I can go to sleep."

Janice walked around to face her. "See that proves it. I knew it when you walked in here talking about an upset stomach. And it's only nine fifteen in the morning and you're ready to go to sleep. You are pregnant, and don't tell me you're not, cause you are glowing."

Lynnette stared at Janice trying to figure her out, but realized that it was impossible to do so. "Janice, will you please take a chill pill. I don't want you spreading rumors about me being pregnant, because that is not the case."

Janice went back to clipping her ends. "If you say so, but I know better."

"I mean it, Janice. I don't want to hear anymore about this, okay? I am not pregnant. Let me hear you say it. Repeat after me. Lynnette is not pregnant."

"Girl, you can't be serious," Janice said.

"I am as serious as a heart attack. Now say it."

"Okay, I'll say it. Lynnette is not pregnant. Are you satisfied?"

Lynnette calmed down a little bit. "Not really, but I guess that'll have to do."

Evangelist Debra Thomas walked in at nine thirty sharp. "Good morning, Ladies."

Janice was putting rollers in Lynnette's hair. "It's a good morning for me and you, but I don't know about Lynnette. She says she has an upset stomach, but I know better."

Lynnette turned around in the chair and looked up at her. "You know something Janice, you are a piece of work. What did we just talk about?"

Janice threw both hands in the air. "What? I didn't say a word."

Lynnette turned back around. "You need to take your mouth to the altar tomorrow."

Debra sat down in the chair next to Lynnette. "What did I walk in on?"

"You walked in on Janice about to get her feelings hurt. When you get to church tomorrow, make sure to lay her whole body on the altar and leave her there."

Janice put the last roller in. "I told you she was in a bad mood."

Lynnette stood up and took off the cape. "I was fine until I got here."

"Okay, Lynnette, maybe you are just sleepy. Get under the dryer," said Janice.

Lynnette sat under the dryer, but before Janice turned it on, she said, "Are you hungry? I have a jar of pickles in the back."

It took all Lynnette had in her to not cuss. ***Get thee behind me, Satan.*** She looked at Debra who was shaking her head from side to side indicating to Lynnette to hold her peace. She looked up at Janice, gritted her teeth, and balled up her lips. "Get away from me, Janice."

"You better watch those mood swings, Lynnette. It's not good for the baby if you're in a bad mood all the time."

Janice turned on the dryer, walked away, and started on Debra's hair. Lynnette closed her eyes, exhaled, counted from one to ten.

Chapter 10

"Thanks for coming, Debra, I really appreciate it." Lynnette escorted her into the living room and they sat on the sofa.

"You're very welcome. You know you can always count on me. I could tell when you called you were upset. I heard it in your voice. So tell me, what has Satan done this time?"

Lynnette wanted to talk, but she couldn't hold back the tears any longer. Lately she had no control over her tears. They fell whenever they felt like it. She reached toward the cocktail table, pulled a tissue from its box, wiped her eyes, then took a deep breath. "It's Gerald."

Debra grabbed her hands. "What happened? Is he hurt?"

Lynnette shook her head from side to side. "No, I'm the one who's hurt."

"What do you mean?"

Lynnette blew her nose and took another deep breath. "He's gone and I don't think he's coming back. We had an argument, he packed a bag, and walked out on me."

"Did you two fight?"

"No. Gerald doesn't fight with his hands. He uses words to strike his blows."

Debra moved closer to Lynnette. "I have to admit I'm a bit amazed. It hasn't even been a full month since your wedding, and you already had an argument and he left. What could have caused this to happen?"

Lynnette took a moment to get her words together. "Well, to sum it up, he told me he's not pleased with my weight and if I didn't lose any he'd divorce me." She could hardly finish her sentence before the tears fell again.

Debra was stunned at the audacity of that statement. To actually marry someone you've vowed to love and cherish forever, then demand that they

34

change their appearance was appalling to her. She grabbed a tissue from its box on the cocktail table and wiped Lynnette's eyes.

"Calm down and relax. Gerald loves you. You may have heard him wrong. Why would he demand something like that of you? There's gotta be something else."

Lynnette blew her nose again. "Oh Debra, there's so much more you don't know."

"I figured there had to be, because this doesn't make sense. Do you want to tell me about it?"

Lynnette paused for a few moments and wondered if she should let the secret out. Keeping it to herself was killing her inside, and she knew she would go crazy if she didn't talk to someone. Unlike Janice, Debra had always been someone in whom she could confide.

"Yeah, I want to tell you everything, but first I'm going to get another box of tissue. Can I get you something to drink?"

Debra declined the offer, and while Lynnette was gone, she took advantage of that time to ask God for knowledge and wisdom. She had never been married, so she prayed that He would anoint her with the right words and advice to give her friend. She didn't want to tell Lynnette to do anything that would add fuel to the fire. Lynnette returned with a new box of tissue and a glass of water for herself. She sat down, opened the box of tissue, and pulled one out. She blew her nose then sat back on the sofa.

"Debra, before I get into this with you, you've got to promise me that not a word of this will ever escape your lips. You've got to take this to your grave, you can't even tell it to the angels, only to God."

"Lynnette, have I ever repeated anything you've confided in me? Have I ever come to you with gossip about someone else?"

"Debra, I know you're someone I can trust, but this is so top-secret and personal I would die if this ever got out. So you've got to put your left hand on the Bible, raise your right hand, and swear to me you won't say anything about this."

Debra looked at her friend. "You know I'm not married, so it would be wrong for me to even consider giving you counsel on a situation on which I have no knowledge of how to handle properly. I'll tell you what I can do for you. I have a friend who is also an Evangelist. Her name is Sheila Collins and she has been married for about nine years. If you want to speak with her and find out what you need to do, I can call her and set up a time for you two to meet. You could also confide in me and trust that if I can't guide you in the right direction, I will speak to Sheila on your behalf, not mention your name, and tell you what she advises you to do. But I have to warn you, this lady is deep, real deep. When you leave her presence you won't know what hit you."

Lynnette thought about that for a moment. "I would really like to talk to her myself, but I want you to be with me when I meet with her. Would you do that for me?"

She gave Lynnette a hug and a smile. "Of course I'll go with you. I'll do whatever you need me to do. That's what friends are for. Where's your telephone? I'll call and see if she's available right now."

Lynnette brought Debra the telephone. "I appreciate you doing this, Deb."

Debra smiled. "It's not me, but it's the Jesus in me."

"No, you didn't steal my motto. It only sounds good when I say it, but since you're such a good friend I'll share it with you. After all, that's what friends are for, right?"

Debra dialed Sheila's number. "Right."

The Answer

God knows how to take a mess and turn it into a miracle. If you're in a mess, don't be too upset because God specializes in cleaning up messes. God is saying some definite things about women being set free and delivered to fulfill their purpose in the Kingdom.

When the Lord gets through working on you, all your adversaries will be ashamed. All your accusers will have to take it back. All the people who contributed to your sense of low self-esteem will have to admit they were wrong. When God gets through unleashing you, you won't have to prove anything. God will prove it. When He gets through showing that you've done the right thing and come to the right place, all the naysayers will drop their heads.

The infirm woman in Luke 13:10-17 was so bound by Satan for eighteen years that she could not even straighten herself up. She had a past that tormented her, but she had a Jesus who set her free. Satan had bound her, but Jesus unleashed her potential.

Many women in the church have not really seen Jesus as the answer to their dilemma. They go to church, they love the Lord, they want to go to Heaven when they die, but they still do not see Him as the solution to their problems.

Can you imagine how hard life was for that woman who was bowed over? Because of her problem, she had to struggle to come to Jesus. Jesus could have walked over to where the woman was, but He chose not to. He wanted her to make her way to Him.

Few of us are crippled in the same way, but we all face crippling limitations. We can be bowed over financially. We can be bowed over emotionally. We can be bowed over with lack of self-esteem. Take that first step. He wants to see you making the effort to reach Him. He wants you to want Him enough to overcome obstacles and push in His direction.

When you see a hunched-over person crawling through the crowd, you will know that person really wants help. That kind of desire is what it takes to change your life. Jesus is the answer.

You may seek help by going from one person to another, but only Jesus is the answer. You may be sick in your body, but Jesus is the answer. If your life is dead, Jesus is the resurrection. It doesn't matter what the problem is, Jesus is the answer!

Chapter 11

When Sheila opened the door, she was happy to see her good friend Debra. "Hey, Girl, how are you doing?"

"I'm blessed. It's good to see you. I love your hair."

"Thanks, I got it cut this morning. John is gonna have a fit when he sees it, but I'll deal with that when the time comes. Come on in."

Debra walked in and Lynnette followed. "Sheila, this my friend Lynnette. She's the reason we're here. She wants to talk to you about some personal matters in hopes of receiving Godly counsel and advice regarding her marriage."

Sheila hugged Lynnette. "Praise the Lord. I pray I can be of help to you in any way I can."

Lynnette felt warmth and comfort in Sheila's hug. "Evangelist Collins, I want to thank you for opening your home to me. I'm struggling in my marriage, I'm very confused about some things, and Debra has highly recommended you. I'm grateful for any advice you may have."

"We are all friends here. We don't have to be so formal with each other. Please call me Sheila." She grabbed Lynnette's hand and led her toward the back of the house. "My husband has an office downstairs. We can go there and not be disturbed."

Lynnette noticed that Debra sat down on the sofa and wasn't following them. Lynnette stopped walking then turned to Debra. "Aren't you coming with us?"

"No. This is a private matter. I'll stay up here until you're done," Debra said.

Lynnette wasn't afraid. She just needed her friend. "I would love it if you came with us. I need your support."

Debra stood up and followed them into the basement.

Downstairs there were Bibles, biblical tapes, and Sunday school books all around. Lynnette wondered how someone could do so much reading. "Sheila, what does your husband do for a living?"

Sheila walked around the desk and sat in John's chair while Lynnette and Debra sat across from her. "He's a car salesman, and he's also a full-time ordained minister of God."

"If you don't mind me asking, how long have you two been married?" Lynnette asked.

"Lynnette, I want you to feel comfortable enough to ask me anything. We've been married for almost nine years and I'll be honest with you, our marriage is wonderful now, but it hasn't always been. John and I have had our share of bad times as much as any other couple, but we are determined not to let the enemy come in and destroy what God has joined together. We focus on keeping the Lord in the center of our love. And by doing that, we found that nothing, no matter how bad it is, can come between us," Sheila said with an encouraging smile.

"Let's have a word of prayer before we get started."

After the prayer, she looked up at Lynnette. "You're having problems in your marriage, is that correct?"

Lynnette felt the tears coming. "Yes."

"I'm about to ask you a question. I want you to listen and think about it for a moment before you answer, because the answer you give will guide us through this session and will give you what you came here for." She sat back in the chair.

"Do you love your husband with the love of God?"

Lynnette was obedient and did as she was told. She thought about it for a moment. Sheila patiently waited for her to answer. Lynnette's mind was working. *Of course I love my husband. I wouldn't be here if I didn't. What kind of question is that?*

"Yes. I love my husband very much."

"That's not what I asked you. You just told me how much you loved him, but that's not the question I asked. I'm going to repeat the question and I want you to think about it again before you answer. This time, I want you to answer what I'm asking you and **only** what I'm asking you. Now listen very carefully. Do you love your husband with the love of God?"

Lynnette sensed some sternness in Sheila's voice. *Who does this lady think she is, talking to me like that? I am a grown woman. I don't have to sit here and be treated like a child.*

Sheila snapped Lynnette out of her thoughts. "Why are you angry?"

Oh my God, please don't let this lady be a psychic. I'm going to get Debra for this. "I'm not angry. Your tone of voice caught me off-guard."

"Your expression shows anger, and you're right, I did change my tone, and I'll tell you why. I have counseled many couples, but mostly women who are like yourself, married and looking for help to repair a broken marriage. When they come to me, they appear to be broken down and mentally beaten up. I sit and listen to them tell me how their husbands have been cruel and unkind towards them. Most times they never admit to any wrongdoing on their own part, or how they could have contributed to the breakup of the marriage. Often the problem is that most women find it hard to surrender themselves to their husbands. After the sessions, they have painted me a picture of huge angry men who set out to do nothing but intimidate their wives. When I get the husband and wife together, the truth comes out. The wife had failed to mention to me how she heavily participated in the arguments and would sometimes be the cause of them. I've learned to be very careful to not allow myself to forget that there are two sides to every story, just like there are two people who make up a marriage. So, if you've come here to talk down your husband or damage his character, I won't allow it. Since you're here by yourself, I will deal with *your* problems. In this session, I will listen to what *you* have to say and I will try and help *you* do what *you* need to do so *you* can be the wife God has ordained *you* to be. And if your husband is willing to come and talk with me, I would be more than happy to sit with both of you and help set you on the path to a successful marriage. But today, it's all about *you* and *your* problems."

Lynnette looked over at Debra who shrugged her shoulders. "Don't look at me, I told you she was deep."

Sheila saw the anticipation in Lynnette. "Do you want to go on?"

She looked at Sheila. "Yes, I do."

"Okay, then answer the question."

"I don't understand it completely. Yes, I love my husband, but what do you mean when you say 'with the love of God'?"

"Thank you for being honest with me. I'll break it down for you." She reached behind her and pulled three King James Versions of the Bible from a bookshelf, placed one on the desk in front of her, gave one to Lynnette, and the other to Debra.

"Turn to Ephesians chapter 5 and look at verses 22 through 24."

All three women found the Scriptures and Sheila read them out loud. "Wives, submit yourselves unto you own husbands, as unto the Lord. For the husband is the head of the wife, even as Christ is the head of the church: and he is the saviour of the body. Therefore as the church is subject unto Christ, so let the wives be to their own husbands in everything."

She finished reading and looked at Lynnette. "Do you understand what this passage of Scripture is saying to you?"

Lynnette read it again silently to herself and looked at Sheila. "I think it's saying I should be faithful to my husband, which I am."

"Yes, it's saying that, but that's not all it's saying. Tell me what's going on in your marriage, then I will reveal to you what these Scriptures are saying."

Lynnette went into great detail about what had been going on between her and Gerald including what he did before the wedding. When she was done, she had gone through half of the box of tissue she brought with her because she knew she was going to need it.

Sheila looked confused. "Why on Earth would you marry him after he told you what he had done?"

Lynnette blew her nose. "Because he came to me and admitted he was wrong and apologized for betraying me. He told me he loved me and he was willing to do whatever it took for me to trust him again. He told me he couldn't live without me in his life, and if I married him, he would love me forever."

"Could it also be that you were only three weeks away from the wedding, the arrangements had been made, and a whole lot of money had already been spent?"

"Yeah, that was on my mind too, but I really love Gerald and he practically begged me to marry him."

"So you felt as though you had no choice, right?"

Lynnette wiped the tears from her eyes. "I didn't want to be embarrassed by calling off the wedding and having to deal with all the questions. My parents, especially my father, would have been so upset. He spent thousands of dollars just for me."

"Lynnette, I don't know your parents, but I'm sure they wouldn't sacrifice their daughter's happiness for anything. Yes, it's every father's dream to walk his daughter down the aisle and give her away to a man who is faithful and true to her, but this wasn't the case. I know for a fact that if your parents had known what happened, they would have told you and everyone else to forget about the money, and would have cancelled the wedding themselves, because your happiness and wellbeing come first. Do you really think your father would've cared about being out thousands of dollars? I don't think so. He would have called off the wedding, no matter how much money was spent, because he loves you."

Lynnette sat there crying. "But Gerald told me he loved me."

Sheila sat closer to the desk and looked into Lynnette's eyes. "Loving you is not sleeping with someone three weeks before the wedding. Love is an action word. When someone loves you, it makes you smile and feel happy. Good lovin' puts you in a great mood. When someone loves you, they are taking care of you."

These last words made Lynnette break down and let it all out. Her pink blouse was ruined with black mascara and eyeliner.

Sheila spoke to her. "When Gerald told you what he had done, did that make you feel good?"

Lynnette answered, "No."

"Did it make you smile and happy?"

"No."

41

"Did it put you in a good mood?"

"No, it didn't."

"Did you feel that he was taking care of you?"

"No."

"Then he didn't love you," Sheila said. She didn't stop there. "And you didn't allow your parents to have an opportunity to show how much they love you. But do you know what the worst part about all of this is?"

Sheila didn't wait for Lynnette to answer. "The real bad part about this, Lynnette, is that you didn't love yourself."

Lynnette wanted to lie down and die. First she got mentally and verbally abused at home by her husband, then she came to this lady for help and was told that she didn't love herself. Maybe this was Lynnette's destiny, to live a life of abuse, defeat, and total destruction. Why else would God allow her to go through this?

She sat there and cried. Debra got up and went to Lynnette. She put her arms around Lynnette's shoulders and wiped her face with her hands. "Shh, it's okay. It's gonna be alright. Calm down." She felt Lynnette's shoulders shaking. "Don't hyperventilate, Lynnette, breathe slowly."

Debra looked across the desk at her friend. "With all due respect, Sheila, she came here to find answers that will help her mend a broken marriage, not to be beaten down some more. Surely you don't think telling her she doesn't love herself is helping her. I think you should apologize."

"Apologize for what? Telling her the truth? Debra, you've known me for how long, about twelve years now? You know how I am. I get down to the nitty-gritty and tell it like it is. I don't sugar-coat nothing."

Sheila looked at Lynnette. "I know what I'm saying to you hurts, but before we started, we had a word of prayer, and I asked the Holy Spirit to give me the words you needed to hear. Before today, I didn't know you existed, therefore I have no reason to bad-mouth or be mean to you. What I'm saying to you tonight is Spirit-led. These are the things God wants you to hear. What I'm telling you now God has already told you, but for some reason you didn't listen."

Lynnette was holding her face in her hands, but after that statement, she looked up at Sheila and froze. She couldn't move. She couldn't even blink her eyes.

Debra saw this and got scared. "Lynnette, are you alright? Lynnette, say something. Snap out of it."

Debra shook her. "Lynnette, what's wrong with you?"

"Leave her alone, Debra, she'll be alright. She's thinking about what I just said. When she's ready, she'll speak. For now, let God work."

Debra went back to her chair and sat down, but she didn't take her eyes off of Lynnette. And Lynnette didn't take her eyes off of Sheila. Lynnette's eyes were wide and red. She stared at Sheila and appeared as though she was ready to leap over the desk and attack, but Sheila wasn't worried. She'd seen that look many times. She knew the Holy Spirit was moving in Lynnette's mind. Debra was a different story. She had never seen anything like that before, and she was afraid. The look in Lynnette's eyes was frightening Debra. Debra looked at the stairs to see how far she was from them, because if Lynnette leaped across the desk at Sheila, she was going to leap up those stairs and out the front door so fast, all you would see was the dust she left behind.

It was a full five minutes before Lynnette blinked her eyes and moved in her seat.

"You know something, Sheila? You are right. God did speak to me, but I didn't know it was Him. I kept hearing voices in my head telling me not to get married and something kept telling me Gerald didn't love me. Now I know it was the voice of God."

"And how do you feel about that?" Sheila asked.

"I feel terrible, like I disobeyed God and ignored Him by doing exactly what He told me not to do, and now I'm paying for it."

"Paying for it how?"

"Maybe God is punishing me for being disobedient. I feel that He hasn't blessed my marriage. Now I know Gerald and I will never be happy because God never wanted us to marry in the first place," Lynnette said.

"Before you allow the enemy to put crazy thoughts in your head, I'm going to stop you there. Yes, God had forewarned you not to get married because He knew what was to come as a result of it. God saw into your future, knew there would be problems with you and Gerald, and He tried to prevent them from happening. However, you didn't recognize His voice in time. So now that you're married and are facing these problems, you've got to deal with them. God gives us free-will to do whatever it is we want to do. He doesn't force His righteousness upon no one. It is up to us as individuals to make the right decisions in life. God is not punishing you because you got married. What's happening is you are now facing the struggles. Don't allow the enemy to make you think God hasn't blessed your marriage, because He has. When you and Gerald vowed before God to love, honor, and cherish one another unto death, it is then that He gave you His blessing. At that moment, it didn't matter to God what happened before your wedding. Once you've said those vows and made the promise and commitment to Him, He blessed it. And along with the blessing, He gave both of you His grace to have a wonderful, prosperous, and Christian life together. Since you two have made the vow to Him, you can't give up. You owe it to God and yourselves to deliver that promise. But you've got to look to Him for the answers. God created marriage, which means it was His idea to take woman out of man and join them together as husband and wife. He also ordained marriage, which means He has given the husband and wife, who are now one flesh, the grace to endure all that would come against them to try and undo what He has done."

Lynnette sat in the chair taking this all in. "So, what do I do now?"

"Love your husband," Sheila said.

"You're saying I've got to love him even though he's treating me bad? I don't understand this," Lynnette said.

"Let's go back to the Scriptures."

The three of them read the Scriptures again. Sheila looked up at Lynnette. "'*Submission*' is a word that is often misunderstood, just like the word '*obey.*' In this particular Scripture, the word '*submit*' means to give yourself freely, to stand by, to obey, and to do for your husband what he asks of you, as long as it is within the will of God. Do you understand?"

"Yeah, I understand, but I don't think what Gerald wants me to do is in the will of God."

"Why not? He wants you to lose some weight. What's the big deal?"

"It's only been a few weeks since our wedding, and already he's trying to change me into someone else, and I don't think that's right."

"What do you mean he's changing you into someone else? Who are you talking about?"

"I'm talking about the woman he slept with before the wedding. She's about fifty pounds lighter than me, and when I went to his church and saw her, he started acting real funny and nervous. I asked him what his problem was, and he gave me some excuse about how hot it was and he needed to get some water. He had the nerve to leave the sanctuary and sit outside where it was even hotter. And it was the very next day that he started this weight crap."

"Lynnette, is it possible he was uncomfortable having his wife and this woman in the same church? Could it be that he realized by the way you were behaving that he shouldn't have brought you there, and it made him nervous? Is there the slightest possibility that because you asked him where she was, and you were willing to make a scene in church, he excused himself so neither of you would be embarrassed? Could any of these things be possible or perhaps true?"

To Lynnette it seemed like Sheila was taking Gerald's side. "Yes, I guess all of it could be true when you put it that way, but why are you defending him? He's the one who left me."

"I'm not defending him. I told you earlier I was going to deal with *you* and *your* problems. Now you may not like this, but I'm going to tell you how all of this is your fault, and I'll show you how you chased your husband out the door, but you've got to be willing to listen and see this revelation. Do you want to hear it or not?"

After all I've told this woman, she's telling me I pushed Gerald out the door. I don't get this. What time is it anyway? I gotta go.

44

"Lynnette, do not let the enemy distract your mind. You came here for help and answers. I told you that every marital problem has two sides to it. You've got to learn to take responsibility for your own actions. You have initiated this problem in a big way, but if you don't recognize this and learn to deal with it, you and Gerald will never get past this point and your marriage will be doomed. The decision is yours. You have to want the help. This is your marriage and your life. You can either listen to what the Lord has to say, or you can walk out of here without the answers you came here for, go back home, make matters worse than they are, and possibly end up in divorce court. You said you didn't recognize the voice of God before your marriage. Do you still want to ignore it after your marriage? You may think that Debra referred me to you, but the truth is, God has brought you here for a reason. Why not sit back and be blessed?"

Even if Lynnette wanted to walk out now, she'd be a fool to do so after what Sheila just said.

"Okay, Sheila, I'm listening. Bless me."

Sheila leaned back in her chair. First, let's come to the understanding God has indeed blessed your marriage. The moment the two of you vowed your promise to Him, He ordained it. Is that understood?"

"Yes, I understand."

"Good. Now from that day on, your past and Gerald's past no longer mattered to God, and it shouldn't have mattered to either one of you. When God sealed that bond, you two became one flesh and started a whole new life together. Is that understood?"

"Yes, I understand."

"Good. Now I'm going to tell you how you brought the past to the present, which is where you went wrong. Are you ready?"

I guess if I'm not ready, I'd better get ready. "Yes, I'm ready."

"You should not have gone to that church. He told you he met this woman in Bible class, so you knew she was a member there. Why would you want to be in the same place as she? I'll tell you why. The enemy was working on your mind. He made you think you had to see her. And when you saw she was beautiful and skinny, he got your mind working. He caused you to look at her and find the difference between the two of you that *you* think would draw Gerald to her. So you took that difference and ran with it. Your emotions were flying high and all kinds of thoughts were going through your head. Then look what happened. You used that against your husband, and totally turned around something he meant to be good..

Let me explain something to you, Lynnette, Satan knew while you were sitting in church that Gerald was going to cook dinner for you the next day, and he knew Gerald was going to approach you about your weight. He figured if he could get you to look at this woman and see how skinny and pretty she was, he could use that to get you angry and upset. So when you saw what Gerald had prepared for you, all Satan had to do was remind you of this woman. Don't you know, if you had not gone to that church, you would never have known what she looked like? Therefore, you wouldn't have used her against Gerald. This woman was his past. It doesn't matter if he slept with her a month ago or the day before the wedding. She was in the past and that's where you should've left her. He has not brought up her name since before the wedding. He has forgotten about her, or at least tried to, but you went back and got her and threw her in his face.

He wants you to lose weight. So what? What has that got to do with her? He said he was concerned about your health. You called him a liar and accused him of trying to make you look like her, but if you had not gone to that church, you would have never known what she looked like, and you would have had no problem *submitting* to your husband's request. It's not like he came home one day and said **'I'm sick of the way you look. You disgust me. Lose some weight.'** Instead, he thought enough of you to stop at the grocery store, shop for you, and cook your dinner. And by doing that, it showed he was willing to do whatever it takes to help you honor his request. But what did you do? You allowed the enemy to have his way with you. It's a wonderful thing to have a husband who's concerned about your health and is willing to cook for you, so you can become the wife he looks forward to coming home to. And the more he told you she wasn't the issue, the more you argued. Has it ever occurred to you that he really intended to make good on his promise when he said he would love you forever, and would do whatever it takes for you to trust him again? Do you think he wants to be reminded of his past? Could it be possible he realized how much he has hurt you, and he's trying to forgive himself, while at the same time doing all he can to earn your trust again? If you've offended someone then asked that person for forgiveness you wouldn't want them to bring up that issue again. If they have forgiven you in their heart, then the past no longer matters. It should be as if the incident never happened. So the bottom line, is you really haven't forgiven Gerald. And now that he's gone, you're sitting around wondering what happened. Is there anything about Gerald you'd like him to change?"

"Well, I would like him to get his teeth fixed," Lynnette said.

"Let's say there was a man who had a great smile, and Gerald saw that this man was always in your face grinning and flashing his pearly whites. One day you make a dental appointment for Gerald, and he jumps all over you, saying you want him to look like **Mr. Mouth Shine So Bright**, and no matter how you tried to convince him otherwise, he continued to tell you different. Wouldn't you think Gerald was behaving ridiculously, when all you were trying to do was make his appearance more attractive to you?"

"I never thought about it that way, Sheila."

"That's because the enemy was having a field day at your expense. You've brought up Gerald's past. Now you've got to make him forget it again."

"How do I do that? He's gone. I don't know where he is, or when he's coming back, if he comes back at all."

"He loves you. He'll be back. His clothes are there. He's gotta come home some time. You've got to change churches for one thing, and find another one you both feel comfortable with. Then submit to him and lose some weight. If he's willing to cook for you, it shouldn't be too hard. Establish a prayer life with him and set aside some time for Bible study together. And no matter what happens, never ever bring this woman up again. Forget she even exists. She's in the past, so let her stay there. Does Gerald have a cellular phone or pager?"

"Yes, he has a pager."

"Go home and clean the house, prepare a fat free meal, run him some bath water, and light some candles. Then page him and tell him you're sorry for the things you've said. Tell him you're willing to lose some weight, that you miss him, and you're waiting for him to come home. When you hang up the telephone, get on your knees, thank God for this revelation, and ask Him to bless you with the capability to love your husband right. After you've done that, put on something sexy, play some soft praise and worship music, and wait by the door for your husband. When he comes in, the first thing he'll see is his wife who's chosen to be ***submissive***."

Lynnette grinned from ear to ear. She could hardly wait to get out of there. "Sheila, I thank you so much, I really do. How can I pay you for your time?"

"Just do what God has told you to do."

Lynnette hugged her and thanked her again, then she hugged Debra, and thanked her for bringing her to see Sheila and for waiting so patiently. They had been there for two hours, and Lynnette was anxious to get home and be with her husband. They said their goodbyes and left.

47

Stand

Since we are born with all sorts of human weaknesses, what are we to do when the devil comes along? The Bible says, "having done all...Stand therefore" (Ephesians 6:13, 14). In Romans 14:4, we read, "God is able to make [you] stand." Not in your strength, but the strength of Jesus Christ. You can't stand in your own strength. All by yourself, you're just another Eve. But in the strength of Jesus, you can stand and not give in.

God's way isn't always easy. It may be the perfect way, the ideal way, the truly "natural" way according to His creation, but you still may have to work at it. Just because something is right doesn't mean it's easy. Some days you need a little more strength than on other days. Every time you need help, run to the Breasted One. He has what you need to move forward.

Your tremors of temptation, your moods and attitudes toward sin, will pass if you will only stand up to them in His name. The blood of Jesus Christ has set you free and will continue to uphold you, if you will just stand on Christ the solid rock!

When the devil shows up with his temptations, announce that you are going to stand in Christ. You're going to stand until the shaking quits, until the thunder stops rolling, until midnight passes into dawn, until you feel peace again, until the wave of loneliness passes, until your marriage is restored, until you come out of debt, until your struggle is over!

When you do the standing, God does the strengthening. Paul said, "I can do all things through Christ who strengthens me" (Philippians 4:13). Christ doesn't strengthen just once. He will strengthen you again and again and again. He will strengthen you every time you face a difficult challenge, every time a memory comes back to haunt you, every time you're reminded of your imperfect past, every time you face a decision.

Drawing from God the strength you need to stand up to the devil may take effort. It may take your praise, your prayer, your getting into His Word with an intensity you've never had before.

But the fact is, you can stand if you want to. So, stand!

Chapter 12

As she rode home from Sheila's house, Lynnette was on an emotional and spiritual high. Never in her wildest dreams would she ever have believed Gerald's leaving was her fault. She understood what Sheila was saying, but at the same time, she didn't understand it at all.

Debra, who was driving, looked over at her. "You're mighty quiet."

"I know. I just can't believe what happened back there. I went to see Sheila expecting to be defended. I just knew she was going to see my situation and have pity on me, but instead she rose up against me and showed me that if I had handled my situation differently, Gerald and I would be together right now."

"I told you before we left your house that Sheila was deep. As long as I've known her, she has been a great problem-solver, because she tells people how they contribute to their own problems. Many people prefer her over their own Pastors because they know she will get to the root of the problem and tell them exactly what they need to hear. A lot of people are intimidated and won't even approach her when they need help because of the way she talks. Sheila is the type of person you can easily befriend, but the minute you sit in her presence in a one-on-one session, you can best believe the friendship goes out the window and the Evangelist steps in and takes over. As a matter of fact, she has lost many friends after a private session because they couldn't handle what she had to say. Instead of taking her advice, they prefer to never talk to her again because she wouldn't cry with or comfort them. You saw for yourself how she didn't need Gerald there to defend himself. She has the gift to listen to the problem and show the person who's doing the complaining how the problem could have been solved or avoided if they would've behaved or responded differently."

"Although I never expected it to turn out this way, I'm glad I went to see her. But I gotta be honest, there were times when I felt like walking out, because it seemed like she wasn't understanding me," Lynnette said.

"You know the saying 'There's nothing too hard for God'? I almost want to say there's nothing too hard for Sheila. She's an awesome woman of God and goes strictly by His book and rules. One thing I admire about her is she never gives her own comments and suggestions, but gives you the word of God, and tells you He said it and that's the way it is. You either obey His word and commandments, or you die."

Lynnette felt a shiver. "That's deep Deb, real deep."

"I know it's deep, but it's the truth and the truth will what?"

They both answered. "Make you free."

"Amen to that, Girl."

Debra pulled into Lynnette's driveway and put the gear in park. "Well, my love, we're here. Are you ready to get your marriage on track?"

"Yes, I'm more than ready. I want you to know if there ever was a friend in this world, you're the one. Words cannot express how grateful I am to you. I cherish our friendship and I love you for always supporting me."

Debra saw the tears in Lynnette's eyes and couldn't stop her own tears from falling. "Don't you know I feel the same way about you? You have been there for me through thick and thin. I walk around with a painted smile on my face sometimes, but it's such a blessing to know I don't have to go through anything alone. Evangelists have a role to play. We must appear we are on top of the world at all times, but we have our struggles too."

"When you struggle, I struggle, and I know that when I struggle, you struggle. That's the blessed bond we share," Lynnette said.

The two friends stared at each other, both crying and sharing a beautiful moment.

Lynnette leaned over and hugged her friend. "You can always count on me."

Debra returned the hugged with a squeeze. "Ditto."

Neither of them wanted to let go of the embrace, but Debra broke away first. "Do you want me to come in and help you get ready for Gerald?"

Lynnette wiped her eyes with her hands. The box of tissue had been used up long ago.

"No, I'm looking forward to doing this myself. I'm going to put on some praise and worship music. I'll be fine, but I thank you for the offer."

"You're welcome. I really hope and pray your marriage will prosper and be what God wants it to be. No matter what happens tonight, hang in there and know God will come through."

"Thank you, Debra."

"Alright, I'm leaving. You're on your own. Call me first thing in the morning. I want to hear all about tonight."

"You know I will."

They hugged one more time then Lynnette got out and went inside the house. Debra sat in the car a moment and prayed to God to let His will be done, and to please send down His anointing and a special blessing on that marriage and others like it.

Chapter 13

The chicken breast baked in the oven, and the lettuce, tomato, and cucumber salad chilled in the refrigerator as Lynnette changed the sheets on the bed. There were strawberry-scented candles burning on the night stand and dresser. She had already taken her bath using the strawberry bath oil Gerald had given her. It seemed funny to her how she never had to tell him that she was running low on the bath oil. Every time she was finishing a bottle a new one would appear on the ledge of the tub right next to the one that was almost empty. Though some people would find it offensive, she loved it when Gerald walked up to her, sniffed her neck, and told her how good she smelled.

She had slipped into a short, black, lace teddy that Betty gave her before she took her leave of absence. Betty told her to only wear it on special occasions. Lynnette thought tonight was a very special occasion, because she was getting her husband back thanks to Sheila. She fluffed the pillows and folded the sheets back nice and neat. She walked into the kitchen, took the chicken out of the oven, then went into the living room and sat on the sofa. Before she paged Gerald, she did exactly what Sheila advised her to do. She got on her knees and asked the Lord for guidance and help to say the right words. After prayer, she went into Gerald's office, sat at his desk, picked up the telephone, and dialed the number to his pager. She added "911" to their home number, wanting him to call immediately. She placed the telephone on its receiver and leaned back in the chair hoping he would call. While she waited, she began to think back on some of the things Sheila said to her that evening. She kept reminding herself it was her fault Gerald had left, and now it was her responsibility to get him back. She made up her mind that if he didn't call she wouldn't give up. She was willing to do whatever it took to get her man back. She remembered that with God all things were possible. It was the third ring that snapped her out of her thoughts.

"Hello?"

"It's me. What's wrong?"

Help me, Lord. "I need to see you."

"You paged me "911." What's the emergency?" Gerald asked.

"The emergency is I need to see you."

"Why now?"

Where are You Lord? "Because I miss you, and I want to talk to you about something."

He took a deep breath and let it out. "I don't feel like arguing with you again. What's the use of coming home if we can't accomplish anything?"

Lord, do You hear me calling You? "That's why I paged you. I want us to work this out. I have been doing a lot of praying and thinking, and realized I was wrong for behaving the way I did. I accused you of some things I shouldn't have, and I want to apologize. I love you and want you to come home."

"I don't have a problem with coming home. What I don't understand is why you can't simply do what I'm asking you to do."

Lord, if You're talking to me, You must be whispering 'cause I can't hear a thing You're saying. "I thought you were trying to make me look like Melanie, and I got angry and jealous, but I know better and I'm really sorry."

He took another deep breath. "Look, Lynnette, there is no Melanie. She is a part of my past I'm trying to forget. She means nothing to me. What I did was wrong and it never should've happened, but I can't change the past. How do you expect me to get over it and get on with my life if you're going to bring her up every time you disagree with me about something? I don't need anyone, especially my wife, constantly reminding me of my sinful past. I love you and only you. Whatever happened is in the past. You are my present and my future. I want us to be together forever, but that's not going to happen if you keep throwing my past in my face. I would rather stay where I am than come back home and fight with you," Gerald said.

Lord, can You please speak up? "Gerald, I can't tell you how sorry I am. I promise to never bring up her name again. I'm miserable without you and I want you to come home. I baked some chicken and made a salad. Tomorrow I'm going to join a health club and start working out."

"Where is all of this coming from?"

"My heart," Lynnette said.

"I think we should start looking for another church home. I know it wasn't easy for you to go there last Sunday and I should've known better. I apologize for putting you through that."

"That's okay, Baby, we can get past that too."

"What do you have on?" Gerald asked.

"You're gonna have to come home and see for yourself."

"I think I smell strawberries through the telephone line."

"I think you do too. Hurry up. I don't want the chicken to get cold," Lynnette said.

"I'm hungry for one thing and it ain't chicken."

"Aah sooky sooky now. Don't you start nothing you can't finish."

"What makes you think I can't finish it?" Gerald asked.

"How can you finish it on the telephone?"

"I'm on my way home. I'll be there in ten minutes."

"I can't wait," Lynnette said.

She hung up the telephone and leaned back in the chair with a smile on her face. "Lord, I couldn't hear You, but he's on his way home."

"THAT'S BECAUSE I WROTE ON YOUR TONGUE."

Lynnette went into the bedroom and got a candle from the night stand, then went back into the living room and sat it on top of the cocktail table, then laid on the sofa and waited for her husband.

Chapter 14

It had been one week since Lynnette and Gerald came to terms with their marriage. She agreed to eat right and lose weight, and he agreed to be Gerald. The very next day after that wonderful night of endless and passionate love-making, Mr. Gerald Hawkins laid down the law. Lynnette was to only eat baked or boiled poultry and steamed vegetables. And today Gerald took Lynnette and introduced her to "Ladies In Motion," a health club for women.

As the instructor escorted them around the gym demonstrating how the equipment was properly used, she explained to Lynnette it is recommended that the cardiovascular machines such as the treadmills, exercise bicycles, and Stair Masters be used for thirty minutes per workout.

"I've never been on any of these machines before. I doubt if I can last for fifteen minutes, let alone thirty," Lynnette said.

"We recommend that on your first try, you should try to become familiar with the machines to establish a personalized workout you create for yourself. It is totally up to you to set your own goals. We caution you to take it slow for the first couple of weeks and then if you're comfortable enough with the machines, you can escalate and really start to challenge yourself. In no time at all, you'll start to burn more and more fat. Then you'll see the thirty minutes will fly by."

Gerald was nice and quiet until this point.

"Lynnette has a high goal. She really wants to lose about fifty pounds as soon as possible. She knows how to walk, and she knows how to ride a bike, since she's been doing them both all of her life. I think an hour on both machines every day would deliver the results she's looking for."

Lynnette literally felt her face go white. ***How dare he speak for me that way***. The instructor quickly put him in his place. Too many times she had seen women join the health club just to please a man. She remembered a time when a woman worked herself so hard spending hours at the gym every day running, swimming, and lifting free weights she actually passed out on the track. She had been pushing herself to the maximum and completely forgot to replenish the water she'd sweat away daily. The ambulance was called and the woman was taken to the hospital and treated for dehydration.

"Mr. Hawkins, I understand you may want to motivate and encourage your wife and be the support she needs as she tries to reach her *own* goal, but if you push her too hard with these machines she could do more harm to herself than good. Thirty minutes on each machine two to three times a week is more than enough exercise for anyone who is trying to lose twenty, fifty or even one hundred pounds. Our machines are set up to give our customers the best cardiovascular workout to get their heart rate up according to their individual body build. We offer an excellent aerobic and step class. I'm sure they would help Lynnette reach her goal and the classes are a lot of fun too."

"When can she get started?" Gerald asked.

Lynnette wanted to run out and never show her face in this place again. *Why can't he just shut the hell up?* If this was his way of showing support, she didn't want it.

"Now that she's had the tour, and if she has no more questions, we can get her registered and she can start immediately."

They followed the instructor back to her office and Lynnette signed all the necessary paperwork. She was officially an LIM member obligated by contract to pay forty-seven dollars a month for the next two years. As she signed on the dotted line she thought to herself, *He wanted me to lose some weight. The least he could do is pay for it himself, but I guess that's too much like right.*

When they were done, the instructor gave Lynnette her receipt, shook her hand, welcomed, and congratulated her.

Gerald stood up. "Okay, let's go and get you some workout clothes so you can start tomorrow."

The instructor said right in front of Gerald, "The good news, Lynnette, is there are no men allowed in the gym while the women are working out. In here, we motivate each other the right way. There is no pressure. And you'll find being here is an opportunity to get away from the stress and troubles that can sometimes be a bit overwhelming. This is a place of solitude where you can be yourself. The bad news is eventually you have to leave and go back home."

Alright, Sister instructor girl. That was well said and hopefully well heard.

It was Sunday morning and if Gerald thought Lynnette was going to the gym to sweat her hair back, he had another thing coming. She decided she would start fresh after work Monday. Sunday was the Lord's day and they had decided it was best if they left Gerald's church, because it wasn't fair for Lynnette to have to look at Melanie's face Sunday after Sunday. Today, they will worship at True Divine Baptist where the Reverend Michael B. Vaughn is Pastor. Lynnette happened to be flipping through channels one night and caught the end of Pastor Vaughn's broadcast on television. He was closing his sermon.

"There is no problem too hard for God. He is a healer and a deliverer," he said.

She watched as he opened the doors to the church and many souls gave themselves to God. She vowed to herself that one day she would visit that church and see what it's about. She told Gerald about the broadcast and he agreed to go with her.

True Divine Baptist was in Melrose Park located on Ninth and North Avenue. Sunday morning worship began at eleven o'clock A.M. and they made it just in time. The church was filled to capacity when they arrived at ten fifty. The ushers had already placed folding chairs down the middle aisle and even those were taken. A tall dark skinned man in a black suit and white shirt escorted them upstairs to the balcony where there were a few seats available.

True Divine was a big church. It easily housed about two thousand people. When Lynnette looked down at the pulpit, she saw three women and six men seated, and assumed they made up the ministerial staff.

Morning worship started on time with the congregation standing and singing the morning hymn. The head Deacon asked everyone to reach in the wooden pockets on the back of the pews in front of them for their hymnals. Today's hymnal was on page sixty-seven entitled "Hold to God's Unchanging Hand." After the morning hymn was sung, another Deacon read a scripture from Psalms number twenty-two, then ended devotion with prayer. Immediately after prayer, one of the Elders walked over to the podium and asked the congregation to receive the True Divine sanctuary choir.

Watching the choir march in and take their place behind the pulpit reminded Lynnette of the church she was a part of for the last five years. Every Sunday morning at ten thirty A.M., the choir at Mount Vernon Missionary Baptist Church would march into the stand singing "Just A Closer Walk With Thee." Lynnette truly missed those days and the Friday night choir rehearsals that would end some time after eleven o' clock at night. And if there was a musical or church anniversary coming up, then rehearsal would run well into the early A.M. of Saturday. Tyrone, the Minister of music, would tell the choir not to make any plans for Friday night, because they all had a date with him and his organ.

Lynnette had a beautiful voice and she knew it. She always gave thanks to God for blessing her with such a wonderful gift. She sang first soprano and Tyrone made sure she had a solo on Sunday mornings because she had the type of voice that would draw people to the altar. People have actually joined the church because of Lynnette's singing. Her voice had the power to reach people's ears and let them know God loves them and has a place for them in His kingdom.

Lynnette loved to sing. She was always walking around the house singing praises to God. She strongly believed if she didn't use the gift God had given her, she would surely lose it. She never listened to secular music, only gospel, which was music that edified and glorified the Lord. Before she got married, she would wake up with a praise song in her heart and go to bed with the same. In her car, gospel music took her to and from work. She kept her car radio tuned to *WGOD* the F.M. gospel station.

While the sanctuary choir was singing, Lynnette thought about something. When was the last time she sang praises to God? When was the last time she woke up to praise and worship music or allowed it to send her off to Sleepville? Even at work she couldn't remember the last time she and **"Edward Primer & the Voices of Joy Community Choir"** sang the afternoon away. What happened? Why she stopped? Lynnette enjoyed worshiping God through song. Singing was her ministry. Where did it go?

Caught up in her own thoughts, Lynnette hadn't realized that the choir sang two selections and had sat down. Pastor Vaughn was welcoming the first-time visitors. He asked everyone who was visiting for the first time to stand to receive a gift and warm welcome from the members who were closest to them. Lynnette and Gerald accepted the bookmark with the church's logo on it, and lots of warm hugs and welcomes. After a response from a visitor, the choir sang another selection, then Pastor Vaughn preached a sermon that he called "This May Be Your Last Time."

Lynnette was mesmerized by what Pastor Vaughn said. She took in every word and knew in her heart he was speaking to her loud and clear. She understood the message. She understood God wanted her in this church today because He had a message for her here. She also knew she had to sing. She knew she had to connect with God again. Somehow, someway, she had lost her praise, and she remembered the promise she made to Debra. Lynnette promised Debra that no matter what happens in her life, she would never stop singing. But she had stopped, and it was about time she got back in touch with the Master.

When Pastor Vaughn opened the doors to the church, Lynnette looked at her husband.

"I wanna join."

Gerald wanted to talk her into visiting a few more times before they joined, but he could tell by the look in Lynnette's eyes that she was going to join today with or without him.

"Are you sure? Maybe we should wait a while longer and see how things are here before we commit," he said.

"I'm already committed to God and I want to join today."

"Why now?"

"You heard what the preacher said. This may be my last time."

Lynnette stood up and reached for Gerald's hand, and to her surprise, he grabbed it, and they both made their way downstairs. They walked up the center aisle hand-in-hand, husband and wife, just as it should be. They both joined on their Christian experience, and after Pastor Vaughn announced three more people who had come as candidates for baptism, he asked them all what area of the church would they like to work in. It didn't take Lynnette long to raise her hand.

"I wanna sing."

Chapter 15

Some people say the first two days of a diet are the hardest. It was Wednesday, and day number three for Lynnette, and all week she had eaten only baked chicken breasts and small salads. At least Gerald was considerate. He ate dinner at his parents' house in the evenings. Thelma, Gerald's mother, called Lynnette at work and asked why she wasn't cooking. Lynnette told her she was trying to lose weight and Gerald thought he was being helpful by not putting Lynnette in the position of having to cook separate meals. Gerald wasn't on a diet and he wasn't about to give up fried food for anything. He told Lynnette he didn't want to tempt her with anything other than what she was supposed to eat. It wasn't that Thelma minded having him for dinner, but every night? Lynnette made sure Thelma understood that she had no problem cooking for Gerald, but he insisted things were done his way.

Thelma told Lynnette she was starving herself and she needed more than just a piece of chicken and salad everyday. She reminded Lynnette that Gerald wasn't a doctor and if she wanted to lose weight properly, she should talk with a nutritionist who would prescribe vitamins and a proper diet for her. She also told Lynnette she was too young and pretty to allow any man to dictate how she should eat.

When Thelma got off the telephone with Lynnette, she knew something didn't sound right. She could tell in Lynnette's voice that she was hiding something. She couldn't imagine why Gerald would put his wife through this change. Lynnette was beautiful, smart, and probably too good for Gerald. Thelma vowed that when Gerald showed up for dinner that night she would give him a piece of her mind. She didn't raise him to be that way. Gerald's father had always treated her with kindness and respect and she wasn't about to let her son disrespect his wife or any other woman. Thelma didn't cook dinner that night. She told her husband David she wanted to go out to eat. When Gerald walked in, she read him from "A to Z" and told him to go home and eat whatever his wife was eating.

Lynnette signed in at the gym at five thirty P.M.

The receptionist was a young girl named Karen. Karen worked at L.I.M. after school from three to eight o'clock P.M. She was a beautiful dark-skinned seventeen-year-old with the perfect seventeen-year-old body to match.

"Alright, girl, three days in a row. Go on with your bad self," Karen said.

"Hey, Girl. How was summer school today?" Lynnette said.

"It would've been great if I didn't have to deal with trigonometry. I can't wait until graduation, then I'll be through with this headache."

"Believe me when I say these are the best years of your life, so try and enjoy them. I wish all I had to worry about was trigonometry."

Karen gave Lynnette a towel and a locker key. "I'll try and remember that when I'm taking my finals. Have a good workout."

Lynnette's heart wasn't into exercising. She kept telling herself she was doing this for herself, but she knew she was doing this to please a man who only wanted to please himself. Sheila told her that if she loved Gerald, she wouldn't mind losing weight. Lynnette kept reminding herself it was her duty as a wife to please her husband. But what was he doing to please her? Every night he'd ask her what and how much she ate that day, ask what exercises she did at the gym and for how long she did them? On Monday night, she told him she rode the exercise bike for fifteen minutes then walked on the treadmill for twenty minutes. He told her she wasn't dedicated and if she wanted to see results, she would have to work harder. He said next Monday would complete her first week of diet and exercise, and she should have lost at least seven pounds, a pound a day. Lynnette looked at him like he was crazy, because he **was** crazy and she knew it.

"Gerald, I think a pound a day is too much. I would actually have to stay on both machines for at least two hours to get those kind of results."

"So, what's the problem? You do want to lose weight, don't you?"

"Of course I do, but I don't want to risk my life doing it."

"Lynnette, all you gotta to do is commit yourself, and you can do anything you want to do. I know if you're dedicated to this you can make it happen, and on next Monday I want to see at least seven pounds gone. I'll be happy if you lost more, but I'll settle for seven."

Later on that night after she said her prayers, Lynnette got into bed and cried. Gerald heard her sniffles.

"Lynnette, nobody loves you like I do."

"You know what, Gerald? That's probably true, because right now I don't even feel like I love myself."

She turned her back to him and cried herself to sleep.

Now it was day three and she was back at the gym. She went into the locker room to change into her gym clothes. Once she was dressed, she walked over to the mirror to pull her hair back into a ponytail. She looked at her figure in the mirror. She was wearing bicycle shorts and a sports bra. Lynnette admired her body. She was shapely and well-built. She didn't have flabby arms or jello thighs. She didn't even have a pouch. She was big-boned, but for her height, she was really well-proportioned. Why couldn't Gerald see that and accept her for who she was? Another woman walked up to the mirror to pull her hair into a ponytail and Lynnette glanced at her through the mirror. This woman was about five feet tall and weighed approximately two hundred and eighty pounds. *Now I know I look good. Gerald has definitely got a problem and I'm not taking his crap anymore.*

Lynnette changed out of her gym clothes and went home.

Chapter 16

All the way home from the gym, Lynnette anticipated on how she was going to tell Gerald she made up her mind not to starve herself any longer or suffer through anymore unnecessary exercises just to please him. No matter what he says or does she had reclaimed her life, and if he didn't like it, it was just too bad. Either he'd accept her for who she was or leave. It was as simple as that. This was a new day for Lynnette and Gerald was in for a new awakening. She was fired up and ready when she walked in the front door.

"What did you tell my mother?"

Lynnette couldn't even get in the door before he confronted her. Gerald had gotten a chair from the dining room table and sat it at the front door to make sure the first thing she saw when she got home was his face.

"What do you mean, what did I tell your mother? What are you talking about?"

"I'm talking about you calling her and saying I'm forcing you to lose weight. What's up with that?"

Lynnette felt dizzy all of a sudden and had to lean against the front door to balance herself. She walked past him and sat down on the sofa. "First of all, your mother called me at work today wanting to know why you were at her house every night for dinner, and I told her the truth about how you suggested I lose weight. I told her what I was eating and how I was exercising and she had a fit."

"It was none of her business. This is between you and me. You shouldn't have told her anything. Now she's mad at me because she thinks I'm treating you bad."

"Well, Gerald, you brought this on yourself. She's your mother and I'm not going to lie to her. Don't get angry with me because she found out what you were doing. She's a smart woman. Did you really think she wasn't going to question why you're eating at her house every night? She was bound to figure it out sooner or later."

"I just don't see why you couldn't tell her the diet was your idea. Now she's not speaking to me."

Lynnette leaned back on the sofa with a satisfied look on her face. "Like I said, you brought this on yourself."

Gerald got up, stood in front of Lynnette, and looked down at her. "I know what you're doing. You're trying to turn my family against me, but it's not going to work."

Lynnette's mouth dropped wide open. She stood up and placed her hands on her hips.

"I'm not trying to turn anybody against anybody. Your mother called me. I didn't call her. Don't try to turn this on me, okay? If she found out how ignorant and stupid you're acting, then that's your own fault."

She got dizzy again but kept on talking. "And from now on, I'm not eating another piece of chicken or working out at the gym. If you can't accept me for me then you're free to go. Now if you decide to act like a real man and come to your senses then maybe we can work this out. Because of you, I've lost my self-esteem and self-respect and I won't be abused anymore. You proposed to me the way I am and you married me the way I am. Just like I accept you for who you are, you've got to accept me for who I am. There are no options. I'm hungry and I'm going to get a hamburger."

"So, it's like that? You're just gonna throw this marriage away over some food? You're not even going to try and make it work?" Gerald asked.

Lynnette walked to the door then turned around and looked at him. "I love you. I really do, and you know it. But I refused to be treated like I'm worth nothing, because I *am* somebody. Even if my own husband doesn't think so."

She walked out the door and got in her car. She was dizzy and didn't know why. Maybe it's because she had eaten only a small salad for lunch. When she got to the fast food restaurant, she ordered a fish sandwich, small fries, and a large Pepsi cola. By the time she got home Gerald's car was gone, and she was glad. She just wanted to eat her fish in peace and go to bed. Tomorrow night was choir rehearsal at True Divine and she looked forward to joining. When she opened the door, there was a pamphlet on the floor in the entryway and she picked it up." ***"Divorce in the 90's"*** was written on the front cover. She closed the door, walked to the kitchen, and put her food on the table. Another pamphlet was in the napkin holder. ***"Divorce in the Christian World."***

Lynnette couldn't believe it. So this is what it comes down to. If Gerald couldn't control her, he'd rather divorce her. She blacked out for a second. She felt dizzy so she walked into the bedroom to lie down. When she turned on the bedroom light, she saw another pamphlet on top of her pillow. She picked it up and read the front cover. *"Love or Leave, What to Do?"* Lynnette tried to hold it down, but she couldn't. She turned to run to the toilet but it was too late.

She decided to leave the Carpet Fresh powder on the carpet overnight. She scrubbed best as she could, and hoped there wouldn't be a stain. Debra blew her horn just as Lynnette finished spraying the bedroom with air freshener.

"Come on and get in. Sheila's waiting for us."

Lynnette walked to the car, but she wanted to crawl to it. She had emptied her stomach completely. She was tired, weak, and still dizzy.

"Thanks, Deb, I'm so glad Sheila would see me this late. I would've driven myself, but I don't think I can drive. My stomach is acting up real bad."

"I was glad you called. I wasn't doing anything but watching television. You want to stop at the store and get something to settle your stomach before we get to Sheila's?"

"No. It's already late. Let's just get there. Maybe we'll stop on the way back."

Sheila took her seat behind her husband's desk in the basement. Lynnette and Debra sat across from her again.

"Sheila, I really thank you for opening your home to me again so late in the evening. I'm sorry if I disturbed you or your husband. Please apologize to him for me."

"Girl, John was asleep when you called, he's asleep now, and he'll be asleep when you leave. If I don't tell him that anyone was here, he won't even know it. And as for me, I've already told you my door is always open to you at any time of the day or night. Whenever you need me, please call. I've been counseling at all hours of the night for many years. If John ain't used to it by now, he should be. So what can I do for you tonight?"

Lynnette looked at her friend who was sitting on her right and saw two Debras. She closed her eyes tight and opened them again, still two Debras. Her stomach turned and she swallowed several times to keep whatever was trying to come up in its place. Sheila asked her if she wanted a drink of water and an aspirin, but Lynnette declined the offer.

"I just got a little upset stomach that's all. So much has happened since I was here I don't know where to begin."

"Since I hadn't heard from you I assumed everything was back on track. What went wrong?"

Lynnette took a deep breath and let out a long sigh. "Well, I did what you told me to do. I went home and paged Gerald. He came home and we talked. I told him I would lose weight if it would make him happy, and I was really willing to do it, but he became outrageous with his demands on how I should do it."

"How so?"

"He only wanted me to eat a small chicken breast and a salad all day and exercise for more than two hours a day. Then he demanded I lose a pound a day and he would actually weigh me every week to monitor my progress. I tried to explain to him a pound a day was way too much and the exercises he wanted me to do were ridiculous. He basically said he didn't care and he wanted to see at least seven pounds gone by Monday. He wasn't eating at home. He figured that was his contribution to helping me lose weight. So he was eating at his parents' house every night. His mom called me at work today and asked why I wasn't cooking for her son. I told her it was Gerald's idea for me not to cook because he had me on a special diet and exercise program, and he said he didn't want to tempt me by cooking two separate meals. She asked me what I was eating and how I was exercising. When I told her, she busted a gut. When Gerald got to her house tonight she went off on him and said he was not welcomed in her home until he got some sense.

And today at the gym, I looked at myself in the mirror and liked what I saw. I tried to do what you told me to, but Gerald is very disrespectful and only cares about himself, and tonight he had the nerve to accuse me of trying to turn his family against him. I'm tired of being treated like a child in my own house, and I'm not taking it anymore, and that's exactly what I told him. He said I was the one throwing our marriage away, not him. That's when I left to get something to eat, and when I got back I found three pamphlets about divorce. He had the gall to leave one on my pillow. Now you tell me, was I wrong?"

Sheila sat back in her chair and crossed her legs.

"No, I don't think you were wrong for standing up for yourself. I was under the impression that Gerald was cooking for you and being supportive in a good way. I never meant for you to go home and get mistreated and abused mentally or verbally. I just didn't want you to bring up the past and make it a part of your marriage. If Gerald wants you to do something that's putting your health at risk, then you don't do it. You did the right thing by standing up to him. I commend you for trying to do what pleases him, but you've got to think about your health. At this point, all you can do is try to talk to him and make him understand how you feel, and try to get him to see a marriage counselor. Remember to stay calm and know you're doing what's best for you, and keep him lifted in prayer. It's possible he's going through something you don't know about. Some things we can't work out ourselves, and it takes the Spirit of the Lord to help us. Can I ask you a crazy question, Lynnette?"

"Sure, what is it?"

"Where did you come from?"

Lynnette wasn't sure if she heard her right. "Pardon me?"

Sheila had a slight smile on her face. She loved catching people off-guard with these types of questions. "You heard me right. Where did you come from?"

Lynnette looked over at Debra and she shrugged her shoulders. "Don't look at me. I don't know where she's going with this either."

"Just think about it for a minute, Lynnette. I'm talking about before you were born."

"From my mothers womb." **Dub**

"Where were you before that?"

"Sheila, you're gonna have to help me out. I don't know what you're talking about."

Sheila stood, walked around the desk, and asked Debra to change seats with her. She pulled the chair closer to Lynnette and grabbed her hands.

"Eternity, Lynnette, you came from eternity. You were with God in heaven and he chose you, not anyone else, to live this life. God knew exactly what He was doing when He took you out of eternity and brought you into time. He knew you were ready to come down and die for Him. He trusted that you could be placed in this situation and still give Him praise. Your only purpose and goal in life is to win souls for Christ and then return to glory. That's your mission. And how do you achieve your goal? By staying focused on God, by looking to the hills from which cometh your help and by knowing you're blessed to go through whatever comes your way. You've got to make it back to glory by any means necessary. Know ye that the Lord, He is God. Sometimes we think we can live our lives the way we want to, but that's not the case, especially for those who are chosen. God sent you here for a purpose. He wants you to tell as many people as you can about His good news, and if you have to go through trials and tribulations while doing it, so be it. You do what you gotta do to get to heaven. When trials come, praise Him for them, because He thought enough of you to overcome them for His glory. And when you do overcome them, that makes you strong enough to help someone else who's going through what you've already conquered. Stuff like that pleases God. You're here to represent Him and His kingdom. Don't let Him down. I can see it in your eyes, you're wondering how you're going to overcome your situation. You do it through your praise. And know this, everybody who goes to church ain't saved. God probably sent you here to save your own husband. So don't give up on Gerald. Trust God and believe He will equip you with the ability to do whatever it is He sent you here to do."

"Sheila, it amazes me how you can tell what's going on in my mind. It's like you're a psychic or something. It's almost scary," Lynnette said.

Sheila smiled at that. "In all my years of counseling, I've never been called a psychic. A guardian angel, yes, a fairy godmother, yes, an invisible shadow, yes, and even a fly on the wall, but never a psychic. I'll have to add that one to my list."

Lynnette knew Sheila wasn't making fun of her, but it still seemed kind of eerie that she knew what she was thinking all the time. "No really, I'm serious. How is it you can tell what my thoughts are?"

"Because this is nothing that I haven't done before. You are not the first person I've counseled with marital problems. When I make a statement, or ask a question that may seem too personal or out of the ordinary, facial expressions change. Sometimes people will come right out and tell me I'm getting too deep. In your case, you just look at me like I'm crazy. However, it's always the same expression."

"Well, I definitely don't think you're crazy, but we've only met recently, and you know me so well."

"Lynnette, we have a loving and caring God. He will never allow you to come face to face with your trials and not supply you with the proper weapons to fight them. He will always guide you to the right source or per-son who's anointed with His word to help you through. I told you the last time you were here it wasn't Debra who referred me to you. It was God who brought you here. You see, Lynnette, warfare is spiritual, but it's manifested in the flesh. James chapter 1 tells us in verse 19 that we ought to be quick to hear and slow to speak, because a soft answer turns away wrath. Get it in your mind that your attitude should be based on how you treat others, not how others treat you."

Lynnette let out a loud sigh. "Sheila, I still cook and clean for Gerald. Ninety nine percent of the time he doesn't even come home to eat. You should see how my freezer is stocked with leftovers. I even have food in my neighbor's freezer. I still wash his clothes whenever he decides to drop them off, not because I want to, but because God tells me I have to do these things. I'm trying real hard to be obedient to God no matter what Gerald does or says to me. But it gets rough sometimes, you know? I have to wonder if it's worth it to me to love him when I know for a fact he doesn't love me. I think back on all those times I felt chills when God was speaking to me, I thought I had the flu or something. But now I know God was telling me Gerald didn't love me. So, I'm confused as to why God wants me to love and care for a man who couldn't care less whether I live or die tomorrow."

Sheila replied, "Because you are now husband and wife. You still have a job to do. For as long as you live, you will never figure out God. His thoughts and ways are above ours. He hasn't given us the mentality to understand everything He does. We can't even guess what He'll do from one moment to the next. Sometimes God will do the total opposite of what we think He'll do. That's why it's best to put all our trust in Him and just do what He says, because it's safer that way. Folks are always messed up because they try and predict what God will do. His every move is not for us to know, because if we could figure Him out we wouldn't need Him. I just told you that your blessings are not based on how others treat you. Think righteous. You must understand the spiritual conflict between born again nature and worldly nature. Understand that people have different personalities and are in transition. Personality is the composite of characteristics. Understand that patience is a quality needed in the life of a saint to properly confront difficult people who must be handled with care. Most importantly, understand that saints are also difficult people who are becoming like Christ. Whether you know it or not, you've been given spiritual authority, which means you have a right to represent the Kingdom of God. It's crucial that you know you've been set up to be blessed. So don't blow it by allowing your emotions and feelings to dictate how you should behave. Get your face into your Bible daily, and I'm not talking about those two or three scriptures you read before work. Really get into it and saturate yourself with His words. Learn how to prophesy for **yourself**. Speak God's blessings over your **own** life. Go before Him butt-naked so nothing on you is covered, and allow Him to restore your soul. Renew your mind every day. Realize that your healing and your deliverance is in your praise. Philippians chapter 4 verses 8 and 9 say *'Whatever things are true, whatever things are noble, whatever things are just, whatever things are pure, whatever things are lovely, whatever things are of good report, if there be any virtue and if there be anything praiseworthy, meditate on these things. The things which you learned and received and heard and saw in me, these do, and the God of peace will be with you.'* Trust me, Lynnette. If you work God's word, it will work for you."

It was one fifteen A.M. when Debra dropped Lynnette off. Gerald's car was not in the driveway. Lynnette vacuumed up the Carpet Fresh powder, then took a shower, and got on her knees to pray. "Lord, I just heard some heavy stuff. I don't even understand it all, but I'm praying for knowledge and wisdom. Please let me be whom You sent me here to be. I don't want to fail You. Wherever Gerald is tonight I pray he is safe. Please guard him with Your angels." After prayer she paged Gerald and got into bed to wait for him to call. She didn't know what she wanted to say to him. She really just wanted to hear his voice. Twenty minutes passed and she paged him again, this time adding "911." Another twenty minutes passed, then Lynnette got out of bed, went into the bathroom, got Gerald's Drakkar cologne bottle, and sprayed his pillow with it. She got back into bed and hugged his pillow to her chest. If she couldn't hold her husband then his pillow would have to do.

It was a beautiful summer day, one she'd never seen before. Women pushing baby strollers, children at play, and birds singing set the mood for a nice walk in the park. Lynnette had no worries. She was a strong, independent, beautiful black woman of God. She loved her job, had parents who cared for her dearly, a church home she wouldn't dream of leaving, and the love of her life recently asked her father for her hand in marriage. What else could she want? Her life was complete in every way. If God never did anything else for Lynnette what He'd done already was enough. In the park, she came upon a bed of daisies. She kneeled down, pulled one from the dirt, and plucked the petals one by one. "He loves me, he loves me not, he loves me, he loves me not, he loves me, he loves me not, he loves me, he loves me not, he loves me, he loves me not."

Not satisfied with the outcome of that count, she pulled another daisy from the dirt. This time before plucking the petals, she counted how many there were on the stem. In total, there were nines petals so when she counted this time she'd make sure the outcome was positive. Smiling she started to count again. "He loves me, he loves me not, he loves me, he loves me not, he loves me, he loves me not, he loves me, he loves me not."

Lynnette was dumbfounded. There were nine petals. She was sure of it. Could she have miscounted? Again, she pulled a daisy from the dirt and carefully counted eleven petals. She wasn't smiling anymore. There was a look of concern on her face..

"He loves me, he loves me not, he loves me, he loves me not, he loves me, he loves me not, he loves me, he loves me not, he loves me, he loves me not, he loves me."

Lynnette lost her balance and fell back on the ground. There was one petal left. Where did it come from? She was absolutely sure there were eleven petals. She knew Gerald loved her, there was no questioning that. But why this? She counted three daisies and all of them wanted her to believe Gerald didn't love her. Why?

"If you let a man control your life and give him all you got that's in you, he'll hurt you real bad. I know what I'm talking about. I've seen it happen too many times."

Lynnette quickly looked over her shoulder. "Grandma?"

No one was there. The entire park was empty. She sat by herself holding the last petal.

Lynnette woke up in a cold sweat. The fragrance in the bedroom had changed from Gerald's cologne to her grandmother's perfume.

Chapter 17

Do not be deceived: "Evil company corrupts good habits." Awaken to right-eousness, and do not sin; for some do not have the knowledge of God. I speak this to your shame.
    1 Corinthians 15:33-34

Simone heard Gerald's pager beeping. She carefully moved his arm from around her waist and walked to his jacket that was lying on the floor under his clothes. She checked to see what number appeared and recognized his home number. She turned the pager off then on again to erase it. She placed the pager back in his pocket and tiptoed back to bed. When she put his arm over her waist she woke him up.

"Where have you been?" Gerald asked.

"Just to the bathroom. Go back to sleep."

Gerald started to get out of bed. "What time is it? I gotta get home."

Simone pulled him back under the cover. "Just stay a little while longer. I promise to wake you in an hour. Please stay with me. I don't want to be alone tonight."

Gerald walked in the door at ten after seven A.M. Lynnette had left for work already. He had just enough time to shower and get to work by eight o'clock.

Chapter 18

My brethren, count it all joy when you fall into various trials, knowing that the testing of your faith produces patience. But let patience have it's perfect work, that you may be perfect and complete. James 1:2-4

All day at work Lynnette felt nauseated. At times throughout the day, she would get dizzy if she stood up too fast. When she got to work, she ate half a bagel with cream cheese then drank a cup of coffee, and it all came up as soon as it went down. For lunch she nursed two teaspoons of chicken noodle soup but the smell of the broth wouldn't allow her to continue. By four thirty she was ready to pass out. The nurse's schedule for the next day had been completed. She called every patient to inquire about the nurse's visit, then sat through an hour and a half meeting with Betty and Mr. Flanigan, the Human Resources Manager. Today was the day Lynnette was to make a decision on which nurse to hire to give home care to children with leukemia. After Mr. Flanigan left the office, Lynnette looked at Betty.

"I know the meeting is over, but just give me a few more minutes. I'm so tired right now I think I'll fall to the floor if I stand up," Lynnette said.

"What's up with the dark circles under your eyes? You could pass for a raccoon," said Betty.

"I don't know. I feel sick and dizzy and I can't keep nothing in my stomach."

"I hope you're not coming down with the flu. Why don't you call Dr. Horback and see if she can get you in this afternoon for a physical."

"It's not that serious, Betty, and Dr. Horback doesn't accept appointments after three thirty. It's probably just a slight cold. I am a little hungry though. I'm sure I'll feel better after I eat something."

Betty looked into her eyes. "Lynnette, you look awful, and if you feel half as bad as you look I think you should go and get yourself checked out. I'll call Dr. Horback and see if she'll take you today."

When Betty picked up the telephone, Lynnette stood up and took it from her hand and placed it back on its receiver. "Betty, please stop. I said I'll be alright."

Not once had Lynnette ever disagreed to this extent with Betty. "What's going on with you, Lynnette? For the past month or so you've been withdrawn. You don't laugh anymore and you look like a dead woman walking. Do you want to talk about it?"

Lynnette was dizzy from standing up so fast and she had to lean both hands on Betty's desk to support herself.

"Betty, all I can say is I'm having some personal problems, but I will work them out. Okay?"

"Okay, Lynnette, I will respect your privacy. However, the patients are my priority, and tomorrow morning you're scheduled to accompany Joyce to pray with little Tasha. It's clear to me that something more than hunger is going on with you. You know the rules. No one who is ill, or appears to be ill, is allowed to visit the patients. They have enough to deal with. I'm giving you a direct order to get yourself checked out today, and I expect a report on your condition first thing in the morning. Is that understood?"

Lynnette stood speechless. She knew Betty was right and she had no choice. Either she get the physical or be relieved of her duties.

"Sure, Betty, whatever you say. You're the boss."

"Don't take that tone with me, Lynnette. You know this is what you've got to do. We can't expose the patients to any more sickness."

"Yeah, I know. I'll see you in the morning." Lynnette went back to her desk.

As a favor to Betty, Dr. Horback agreed to see Lynnette right away, but Lynnette thought going to see Dr. Horback was a waste of time. She knew why she was sick and couldn't stand the smell of food. The fact that she threw up coffee and a bagel confirmed it. She sat at her desk, looked at the calendar on the wall, and started to count. The days on the calendar revealed to Lynnette that she had gone eight weeks without a period. Two whole months had gone by and she hadn't even realized it. *So nosy Janice was right after all.* And when Janice finds out that for once in her life she actually knew what she was talking about, she would never let Lynnette forget it. Lynnette could already hear the "I-told-you-so's." When Dr. Horback came back into the examining room, Lynnette had tears in her eyes.

"Why the sad face? I've got great news, Mom."

The **"M"** word pushed the tears out. Lynnette got up from the table, grabbed her things, and left the room without saying a word. Dr. Horback didn't know what to think.

Chapter 19

My heart is steadfast, O God, my heart is steadfast; I will sing and give praise. Awake, my glory! Awake , lute and harp! I will awaken the dawn. I will praise You, O Lord, among the peoples; I will sing to You among the nations. For Your mercy reaches unto the heavens, And Your truth unto the clouds. Be exalted, O God, above the heavens; Let Your glory be above all the earth.
Psalms 57:7-11

Lynnette pulled into the driveway, turned the engine off, and leaned her head against the headrest. "Lord, You've given me a wonderful gift, but I've got no one to share it with."

The sanctuary choir at True Divine Church rehearsed every Thursday night at seven o'clock. They were preparing for the choir's annual fall concert to be held on the first Sunday evening in October. Last Sunday morning, Lynnette read in the church bulletin that anyone who was interested in joining the choir should do so by the last Thursday in July, or they would have to wait until after the fall concert.

She went inside, took a shower, then ate a bowl of oatmeal. Although the oatmeal didn't come back up, she still felt a bit nauseated. She went into the bedroom and lay across the bed hoping the sickness would soon pass. Choir rehearsal was the furthest thing from her mind. Not only did she have morning sickness, she also had afternoon, and evening sickness. She had many friends and family members who've had babies, and they were all different when it came to being sick. Some were only sick through the first trimester, but some were sick longer than that. Her mom once told her that when she was carrying Lynnette she was sick the entire nine months. Lynnette closed her eyes and prayed that pregnancy symptoms were not hereditary. Just when she was dozing off, the telephone rang.

"Hello?"

"Hey, Girl, it's me. Did you decide what song you were going to sing tonight?"

Lynnette quickly sat up on the bed. "Oh my God. Deb, I completely forgot about choir rehearsal tonight. I had a rough day and I had just lain down to prevent a headache."

"Well there's always next week," Debra said.

Lynnette really wanted to sing for the concert, and if she didn't go tonight she would have to wait until October .

"I wish I could wait until next week, but after tonight the choir is closed until after the concert. I guess I'll have to press my way. It starts at seven. What time is it now?"

"It's about six fifteen, so you better get moving. We haven't talked in a few days so I just called to check on you. How's it going?"

"It ain't. And just when I thought I had enough to deal with, guess what I learned today?"

"I can tell by the sound of your voice it's not good. What is it?"

"I'm with child, and don't congratulate me because I'm not happy about it."

"Well if you want me to say that this is not good, I won't. All children are miracles. You say you don't believe that Gerald truly loves you, so look at it this way, God gave you someone who *will* love you. And just think about it, this baby will never try to change you. He or she will love you for you because you're his or her mommie. And remember what the Bible says about all things working together for the good of them who love the Lord. Don't you know that His word is unadulterated, everlasting, sinless, perfect, and incorruptible? It's right there in Romans chapter 8 verse 28. Focus on the words '*in all things*.' Good things and bad things, God is in control of them all. He can redeem things intended for evil, transforming them into good. This is for those who love Him. You do love Him, don't you, Lynnette?"

"Of course I love Him, Debra. You know that."

"Well okay then, this promise is for you. The rebellious souls can't depend on everything achieving something good in their lives. The good God desires to work in those who love Him, including you, is spiritual and eternal. It prepares us for future glory. Do I gotta go to church on you?"

"Yeah. Teach me something," Lynnette said.

"Remember in the last chapter of Genesis when Joseph's brothers were nervous about how Joseph was going to treat them when they purposely tried to hurt him? They bowed before him saying how sorry they were and that they were now his slaves. See, they knew they wronged him and thought Joseph would hold a grudge and retaliate, but look what happened. Joseph was cool about everything. He told them he was in God's favor and all that they had done to hurt him, God intended it for good, to save lives, which is exactly what happened. Then he told them to calm down and relax, because he was gonna provide for them and their families. Joseph stood on the word of God and that's exactly what you gotta do. You told Sheila you wonder if it's worth it to you to hang in there and continue to love Gerald. I'm telling you yes, it is worth it. People who dwell on their tribulations and sorrows can never reap the blessings because they can't see past the hurt and pain. But let me tell you something, Sister girl, those who have a one-track mind that focuses on God and what He can and will do through their sufferings will be strengthened. You can tune in to His resources which allow Him to make good out of the bad. You can find that in Romans chapter 5. Sheila told you God took you out of eternity and brought you into time to live this life. That means you were predestined. Then He called you. Going back to Romans chapter 8 verse 28. Those who love Him have been called according to His purpose. But He didn't stop there. Guess what He did then."

"What?" Lynnette asked.

"He justified you, Girl. That means you were made righteous through Him. He did that when He chose to carry that tree on His back. His blood paid a high price for your justification. It didn't come cheap."

"Debra, you're about to make me run through this house."

"Hold on a minute. I ain't finished. I'll tell you when to run. God still wasn't finished with you. He also glorified you. He made you great and wonderful. So, now that you know you have been first predestined, second called, third justified, and after all of that, glorified, you are in God's favor. He doesn't do all of that for just anyone, only for those who love Him. I beseech you to stay in His perfect will. Yes, it's worth it to keep loving, keep crying, keep praying, and most of all, keep praising. We as saints may sometimes lose confidence in ourselves, but we should never, under any circumstances, lose confidence in God's capabilities. He comes just in the nick of time. Right at the exact moment when we think we're at our breaking point is when He snatches us out of the devil's grip. And one of these days Satan is gonna look for you and won't be able to find you, because you are untouchable and protected. Guess what, Lynnette?"

"What, Debra?"

"Now you can run."

Lynnette immediately dropped the telephone, hopped out of bed, and ran through the house shouting out praises to God. She went from the bedroom to the living room, through the dining room to the kitchen, speaking in tongues and clapping her hands. When she got back to the telephone, she had to wait to speak, because she could hear Debra shouting and praising God herself.

When Debra got back to the telephone, she was out of breath. "You there?"

"Yeah, I'm here, Debra. I am outdone. Listening to you minister to me confirms God does have His hands on me. I remember times like when I was driving on the expressway, I could hear Satan's voice tell me that if I would just make a quick left while going sixty-five miles an hour and hit the concrete barrier, it would all be over. Or while I'm at home having a pity party, a thought would come to me that if I turn on the gas in the kitchen, close all the windows, and sit at the table, and lay my head down, no one would find me until it's too late. I know if it had not been for God's grace and mercy, I'd be in Hell right now. Thanks to you, I know now Satan is trying to destroy me. It really has nothing to do with Gerald. Satan is smart. He has a job to do and he does it well. He's using Gerald, who has no clue he's being used, to shatter me. Satan knows that I absolutely adore my husband, and when I'm honest with myself, I see that I practically worshiped him. And that was a huge mistake on my part because I've placed him ahead of God. Gerald is flesh just like you and me, but my battle is between the Holy Spirit and Satan. I can't fight it, so I have to give it to the Lord and let Him handle it."

"Girl, how did you miss your calling?"

"What are you talking about?" Lynnette asked.

"Do you hear yourself?"

"I'm just telling you what has been revealed to me. It's so clear to me now, Debra. It's like all of a sudden, a light bulb has been turned on in my head. I've got to be very careful what I allow myself to be led into. You're absolutely right. I have been called by God to do His will and Satan knows that. So, he'll use whatever he can to turn me around, even the one person who is everything to me. My husband is my heart and he's precious to me. So it's quite natural he's picked by the enemy to tear me down. But I've got a new revelation today, so it ain't gonna happen. Not in this lifetime," Lynnette said.

"Good for you, Girl. It sounds like you're on the right track, but here's your test. Hang up the telephone so I can call you back."

Lynnette placed the telephone on its receiver and it rang ten seconds later. "Hello?"

"Hey, Girl, I haven't heard from you in a couple of days so I just called to see how things are going."

"It's all good."

"There you go. That's exactly what you're supposed to say. Now back to this baby, I know a couple who were struggling with their marriage and a child miraculously brought them closer than ever. Who knows, this may be just the thing to help you and Gerald or maybe it isn't. I was never one to believe that a child was a mistake. They bring joy and happiness. You know for yourself it's a wonderful feeling to be blessed by God and you, my sister, are truly blessed. Accept your pregnancy and use it to your advantage. Know in your heart that even in the midst of what's going on around you, the High Priest has personally touched your womb. Do not allow the enemy to make you think this isn't the right time to be pregnant. When you and Gerald were intimate, you were loving each other, and during that moment a child was created in love. God gives many gifts, but the gift of life is a miracle. Trust God and go in the direction He's leading you. He has already worked this out. All you've got to do is believe. That's my advice to you, my sister," Debra said.

Listening to Debra made Lynnette's eyes go from crying tears of sorrow to crying tears of joy.

"Do you know how much I thank God for you? I don't care what happens, you are always there to point out the silver lining in every dark cloud. How is it that you are able to do that? I know if I looked up the word 'friend' in the dictionary there would be no words, just your face and telephone number. What have you got to say for yourself?" Lynnette asked.

"You know the saying. It's not me but it's the Jesus in me," Debra said.

"I have to admit I do feel much better about this baby. Thank you, Debra, for always being there for me."

"It's my pleasure. Now you can go and use another gift God gave you."

"What's that?" Lynnette asked.

"You're voice, Girl. You sing like a canary and you know it."

Lynnette smiled. "Yeah, I can do a little somethin', and speaking of singing, anybody who wants to join the choir has to audition. I better think of a song real quick."

"Pick me up on the way. I feel like getting my shout on tonight," Debra said.

"I'll be there in twenty minutes, so be ready."

Dawn Roberts, the choir director, stated that the auditions would take place before rehearsal. She instructed those who were there to audition to sit on the front middle pew. Lynnette heard the instructions just as she and Debra were walking into the sanctuary, and since she was the last to sit, she would be the last to sing. There were two men and three women auditioning. The choir was already seated in the choir stand when Lynnette arrived. Dawn told the five who were auditioning that the purpose of the auditions was to determine where she would place them in the choir. She wanted to listen to their voices and place them where they were most needed. She told them this was not to embarrass or reject them. No one is rejected, but some people had strong voices and others had soft voices. The auditions let her know exactly where to place newcomers.

The tenor section held two women who thought they sang alto until Dawn heard their voices. Now the alto section sounded like altos and the tenor section sounded like tenors.

Dawn called for the first man to come up and sing any gospel song of his choice, and she made sure he heard the word '*gospel*' because one time a young man walked up to the microphone and started singing "Let's Get It On." Dawn had to walk over and take the microphone out of his hand. He was really into it. He had his eyes closed and was swaying from side to side like he was slow-dancing with somebody at a "quarter party" in a basement lit by a red light bulb. Listening to him sing took Dawn way back. But she wasn't about to backslide, so she had to stop him. She heard enough to know he was a good singer, and now he's one of her key soloists. From that day on, she made sure that whoever auditioned was aware that this was a church choir that sang only *gospel* songs.

When the first man came up to the microphone she told him that if he chose a song the choir knew they would join in, and if he wanted to sing a solo that was fine too. After their auditions, Dawn placed the first four new-comers exactly where she wanted them, and now it was Lynnette's turn.

Lynnette wasn't nervous, but she wished she had gone first. She stood up, took her place behind the microphone, and looked at Debra, who gave her two thumbs up. Lynnette had sat through four auditions and still hadn't decided what song to sing. She stood behind the microphone with her eyes closed, asked God to give her a song, and He did. From the moment Lynnette opened her mouth, Dawn and everyone else knew she could hold her own.

She sang a song that had never been heard before. It was her own personal praise song. Through the song, she glorified and magnified God for all He's done for her. She told God she didn't understand why she was going through trials, but whatever the outcome, she would continue to praise Him.

The organist tried his best to follow Lynnette, but it was impossible. She was doing her own thing. One moment, she was calm and mellow, and the next, she was on top of a first soprano note he was sure his organ didn't have.

As it turned out, Lynnette didn't even need accompaniment. The girl was bad. Through her song, she rededicated her life to God and welcomed His presence. When she finished singing, she opened her eyes to see a standing ovation. Debra was in a corner doing what she came to do. Dawn walked to Lynnette and hugged her tight. She commended Lynnette on her beautiful voice. Everyone was standing and clapping, except for one lady in the soprano section, whom Lynnette was placed right beside.

When the auditions were over, Dawn explained why she placed the new-comers where she did. She sat them next to people who had a soft or a strong voice. She placed the two new tenors who had soft voices next to the men who were the strongest so the sound would balance out. Lynnette's voice was strong and very good. She could actually hold the soprano section by herself, and that's exactly what Dawn told the choir. Needless to say, Simone didn't like that at all. When Lynnette sat down next to her Simone was too salty.

Chapter 20

Trust in the Lord, and do good; Dwell in the land, and feed on His faithfulness. Delight yourself also in the Lord, And He shall give you the desires of your heart. Commit your way to the Lord, Trust also in Him, And He shall bring it to pass. He shall bring forth your righteousness as the light, And your justice as the noonday. Psalms 37:3-6

It was only a few minutes after ten o'clock when Lynnette got home from choir rehearsal. To her surprise, Gerald's car was in the driveway. She was still on a spiritual high and in a very good mood. She opened the door and didn't see him in the living or dining room. She assumed he had already gone to bed but wished he hadn't, because she wanted to tell him how good choir rehearsal was. She walked to the bedroom, and saw that the door was cracked open a bit and the light was on. She placed her palm on the door to push it open, but Gerald's voice stopped her in her tracks.

"I can't stop her from joining the choir, Simone."

Lynnette stood outside the door puzzled, because no one besides Debra knew she wanted to join the choir. *Who is Simone and why is she trying to get Gerald to keep me out of the choir?*

"What do you want me to do? I can't chain her to this house and keep her from going to church. I told you when we first joined that she wanted to sing. That's what she loves to do. If you can't handle it, tell me now and we can forget this whole thing," Gerald said.

Lynnette started to sweat. When she removed her hand from the door it left a wet print. She wanted to walk in the bedroom and blow his cover, but she was paralyzed from the waist down.

"I don't know what I'm going to do. You knew that my situation was complicated when we met. I don't need this pressure. What I need is time to think this through," Gerald said.

Lynnette's heart beat so fast she was sure Gerald could hear it.

"I don't like this anymore than you do, but I have to make sure I'm doing the right thing. Listen, I gotta go, because if you're home from choir rehearsal, then Lynnette should be here soon."

Lynnette couldn't believe it.

"No, I can't make it tonight. I'm tired and I have to be at work early in the morning. I'll try and come by tomorrow night," Gerald said.

Lynnette felt sick. She was nervous, upset, and nauseous. Never in her wildest dreams would she ever have imagined Gerald was capable of something like this. But why not? She told herself before the wedding not to trust him, because if he did it once, he'll do it again. She thought about a saying she once heard. "If you fool me once, shame on you. If you fool me twice, shame on me."

This mess was her own fault. She didn't have the right to be upset with him. Gerald was just being Gerald. She walked into this hell hole with both eyes wide open. She was the fool, not him.

She stood outside the bedroom door wondering who Simone was. *Obviously she was someone at True Divine Baptist, but how can that be? We've only been members for one week. Could this be why he tried to talk me out of joining the church?*

Lynnette ran into the bathroom and threw up the oatmeal. She washed her face and brushed her teeth. Gerald came out of the bedroom and looked at her. He didn't even ask why she was throwing up. He went straight to the kitchen and got a glass of water. Lynnette walked in behind him and sat down at the table.

"Gerald, we need to talk."

"So talk," Gerald said.

"Who were you on the phone with just now?"

"A friend."

"What friend, Gerald?"

"Somebody from work. You don't know him."

He has the gall to stand there and lie to my face.

"I heard you tell somebody named Simone that you can't stop me from joining the choir."

"No, you didn't," Gerald said.

Unbelievable. Amazing. This joker is crazy.

"Gerald, I was standing outside the door and I know what I heard."

"No, you don't."

Not only was he telling a bald-faced lie but his voice was low and soothing, like a doctor trying to keep a psychotic patient calm, and that angered Lynnette more than the lie he was telling.

"I'm not crazy. I know you're messing around with somebody at True Divine and I also know she was at choir rehearsal tonight."

Gerald sat his glass on the counter and started to walk past Lynnette. She got up from the chair and blocked his way out of the kitchen. "I'm pregnant."

Gerald's eyes grew wide, and before Lynnette knew it, he had her pinned up against the refrigerator by her throat.

"You're trying to trap me. You'd do anything to keep me in this marriage wouldn't you? But I don't care what you say. I want out. You always talkin' about the devil this and the devil that. Well let me tell you somethin.' I know it's the devil, but I don't care. If he wants this marriage then I'm gonna give to him."

He let her go and she fell to the floor gasping for air. He stepped over her then turned around and looked down at her. "It probably ain't even mine."

Gerald went into the bedroom, got undressed, and into bed. Lynnette got up and stumbled to the sink and filled a glass with water and drank it. By the time she finished showering, Gerald was snoring lightly like nothing ever happened. She stood there watching him breathe.

This fool is a psycho for real. Lord, what am I going to do?

She lay next to him crying silently knowing he was dangerous. If he put his hands on her once he'll do it again and again. She read too many articles on domestic abuse. Some women woke up to more abuse and some women didn't wake up at all. She lay on her back looking at the ceiling.

"I need to hear from You, Jesus."

"I AM THAT I AM."

Bondage on the Inside

A spirit of infirmity may not always represent a bondage that another person places on your life. It may represent a bondage on the inside. And you can't walk away from that kind of bondage. It will keep you locked up until you quit agreeing with the person who has mistreated you.

So many people have made it their life's work to change somebody's opinion about them. They are determined to prove that they are valuable in that other person's eyes. Their consuming ambition is to show somebody that they are good, that they are fine Christians, that they are important.

Never allow another person's opinion of you to become your goal. The fact is, some folks might never like you. They may never approve of you or think you're good enough. They may never change their opinion of you.

If you agree with the person who rejects or abuses you, then you put yourself into bondage to that person. If you say, "You were right to hit me-I deserved to be hit. You were right to leave me-I deserved to be left. You were right to hurt me-I deserved to be hurt"... then you are tying yourself up with their opinion of you rather than tying yourself in to God's opinion of you. When their opinion of you becomes your bad opinion of you, you've built a prison inside your soul with only one prisoner-you. Are you prepared to deal with the fact that the person you've spent your entire life trying to impress may never be impressed? Are you prepared to face the reality that, from God's perspective, it doesn't matter?

If you are going to deal effectively with people in this world, you must be able to work right alongside others without allowing yourself to be controlled by them or governed by their opinion of you. Likely, the deliverance you need most is not a deliverance from the devil or a deliverance from another person. The deliverance you probably need most is a deliverance from some faulty notion you have in your own heart and mind. Be loosed!

Chapter 21

Lynnette woke up before Gerald and immediately made her way to the toilet. She made a deal with God that if He took away the sickness she would never ask Him for anything else for as long as she lived. It was about five minutes to six and time for Gerald to wake up. She turned on the radio when she went back in the bedroom. There was a time when she and Gerald would awaken to gospel music and sing whatever song was on the air until it went off, then they would get up and get ready for work. But this morning was so very different. When Gerald heard the radio, he reached over and turned it off.

OK, he's waking up on the wrong side of the bed.

"Gerald, it's six o'clock, time to get up."

He lay there pretending not to hear her. She walked over to his side of the bed, sat down next to him, and whispered softly, "Gerald, wake up or you'll be late for work."

He thew the covers off, went into the bathroom, and slammed the door shut. When he came out of the bathroom, Lynnette was sitting at her vanity moisturizing her face. She saw him through the mirror getting dressed. "Do you want some breakfast?"

He didn't respond. He was behaving as though she wasn't there. Once he was dressed, he put his wallet in his pocket, and walked out of the bedroom. He didn't even look at her. The next thing Lynnette heard were tires burning rubber and screeching down the street. She looked at herself in the mirror.

"You are a beautiful black woman and don't ever let anyone, no matter who it is, convince you otherwise."

It started to rain heavily as she drove to work, and she remembered how crazy Gerald was driving. "Lord, please keep him safe."

Immediately she got sick and had to pull over to the curb. She opened the door and threw up.

"YOU'RE TOO WEAK TO MAKE DEALS WITH ME."

She was feeling awful, but she had to laugh at God. She looked at the clock on the dashboard and it read six thirty five. "It ain't even been a good hour, has it God? That just goes to show I can't get along without you. What in the world was I thinking? But now that the deal is off, how about taking the sickness away anyway, huh?"

Lynnette was in the middle of reading Ephesians chapter five when it dawned on her that she didn't wait around long enough to receive a medical report from Dr. Horback, and Betty was expecting it to be on her desk this morning. Lynnette wrote, "I'm pregnant and grumpy. Leave me alone and nobody gets hurt," on a yellow Post-It note and stuck it on top of Betty's telephone. Betty had a great sense of humor and would laugh the minute she read the note, but Lynnette actually meant what she wrote. She just wanted to do her job and go home. She cleaned out her voice mailbox then went to pull some files. When she returned to her desk, Betty was sitting in her chair smiling. She held up the note for Lynnette to see. "Now I know why you've been acting so funky lately."

"Me, funky? Never."

"Girl, please. I was going crazy walking around this office looking behind file cabinets and under desks for something that may have died. I even stayed late last night and cleaned out the refrigerator in the break room because the office was smelling like hot garbage. Then I got your note today and realized that the only thing funky around here is your attitude," Betty said.

"Ha ha, very funny, and if I'm the one who's pregnant, why am I standing and you're sitting in my seat?"

"Well, excuse me. Your chariot awaits you." She got up and held the chair out for Lynnette. "I can tell already that this is going to be a long nine months. I better buy some patience."

"Save yourself some money and only buy seven months worth. You've already survived the first two," Lynnette said.

Betty sat stunned on Lynnette's desk. "You've been walking around here pregnant for two whole months and didn't tell me until today?"

"No, it's not like that at all. I just found out myself. I wasn't trying to hide anything from you, so don't have a hernia, calm down."

"Well how do you feel? Was it planned? What did your husband say?"

Lynnette really didn't want Betty to know about her problems, but she was tired of hiding her feelings.

"I'm sick every second of the day. We weren't purposely trying to have a baby, but we weren't using anything to prevent one either, and my husband says this probably isn't his baby. What's for lunch today?"

"How about piz..." Betty almost fell off the desk.

"What did you say?" Betty asked.

Lynnette knew that if she looked up Betty would see her tears, so she opened one of the files and pretended to read her notes. "You heard me right."

"No, I don't think I did and I don't want to believe what I thought you might have said. Tell me again."

She saw tears streaming down Lynnette's cheeks. She placed two fingers under Lynnette's chin and turned her face toward her own. "Are you serious?"

Lynnette nodded slowly.

"Why would he think something like that? You two just got married."

She confided in Betty and told her everything.

"Oh Lynnette, I'm so sorry. I can only imagine what you must be going through. Maybe you and Gerald should see a marriage counselor."

"I've been going to see a marriage counselor for the past two weeks, and she's great, but getting Gerald to go with me would be like chewing steel. It's just not possible since he's so convinced the problem is me. But I believe God is going to do a miraculous thing, and Gerald and I will come out of this triumphantly. It just hurts so bad in the meantime."

Betty pulled a tissue from a box on the desk and wiped Lynnette's face. "I'm not pregnant or married, so I won't pretend to know what you're going through, but whenever you need to talk about it, I'm here for you, day or night. Always remember that."

Betty offered to go in her place to pray for little Tasha, and Lynnette took the rest of the day off.

Chapter 22

And who is he who will harm you if you become followers of what is good? But even if you should suffer for righteousness' sake, you are blessed. "And do not be afraid of their threats, nor be troubled." But sanctify the Lord God in your hearts, and always be ready to give a defense to everyone who asks you, with meekness and fear; having a good conscience, that when they defame you as evildoers, those who revile your good conduct in Christ may be shamed. For it is better, if it is the will of God, to suffer for doing good than for doing evil. I Peter 3:13-17

Vivian was knee deep in dirt. Gardening wasn't her favorite chore. However, she did what she had to do to keep her lawn and landscaping featured in the *Tidy Homes and Lawn* magazine.

Lynnette saw a water hose, shovel, and flowers that were to be planted lying in the driveway, so she parked across the street. Vivian heard Lynnette walking up the driveway, turned to look at her, then went right back to pulling weeds without saying a word.

"Hi, Mommie."

Vivian didn't look her way. "I'm not talking to you."

Lynnette walked passed her mother and sat down on the porch swing. It was early in the day and already about eighty degrees. Lynnette went into the house, got a cold glass of lemonade, returned to the swing, kicked her shoes off, and started to sway. Vivian kept on working.

"So why aren't you talking to me, Mommie?"

Vivian answered her daughter's question but didn't look up or stop working. "You don't call, you don't return any calls, you don't come by anymore, and not once since you've been married have you invited me and your father over for dinner."

"You're both invited over tonight, Mommie, okay? We're having one leaf of lettuce, and between the three of us, we'll split a cucumber. Bring your own bottled water because I don't have any."

Because of the tone of Lynnette's voice, Vivian stopped working and looked at her. "What?"

"Nothing, Mommie, how's Daddy?"

"If you would've called or come by in the last two weeks, you'd have known he hurt his back playing golf last weekend. But he's okay now. He went back to work today."

"Mommie, all you had to do was leave a message on my voice mail or call me at home. You know what time I get home every night. Why didn't you call me there?"

"I did call you at home. I talked to Gerald twice and told him about your father. He said that he would give you the message, but maybe he forgot."

Yeah, I bet he forgot alright.

"I even left you a message at work to call me, a whole bunch of times."

"Mommie, if you had your way, you'd talk to me all day. Do you remember the message you left with the receptionist telling me to call you because it was an emergency? Well she came and got me out of a very important meeting. When I called you back you only wanted to know if I was wearing the red blouse you bought me. To me, that's not an emergency. Daddy hurting his back is an emergency, and I definitely want to know about those things. But I can't call you if you only want to talk about what you heard the neighbors arguing about, or if you should or shouldn't go to bingo. If you want to go to bingo then go. I go to work to work and I take my job seriously. I have a lot of people who depend on me and I don't need a lot of unnecessary distractions."

Vivian stopped working again. "Well excuse me for interrupting your day at work, Honey. I didn't know I was being such a pain."

Lynnette closed her eyes and exhaled. "Mommie, you're not a pain. I enjoy talking to you. I just want you to understand I can't talk to you all the time while I'm working."

Vivian pulled the weeds faster. Lynnette knew too well that when her mother was upset she'd clean the house quickly. Lynnette never understood why she did that.

"Okay, Mommie, how about I call you everyday on my lunch break? Then we can talk for a whole hour about anything you want, and I promise to come by here every Friday after work to see you and Daddy. Is that alright?"

"As long as I won't be interrupting anything."

Lynnette caught the sarcastic tone and wanted to come right back at her mother with one of her own but decided to let it go. Had it been Gerald who said something like that, she would have fired back.

"No, Mommie, you wouldn't be interrupting anything. Now come and swing with me because I need to talk to you about something."

Being the mother she was, Vivian couldn't help but let the tears fall as she sat and listened to her daughter describe the way her marriage had turned out.

"Baby, you don't have to stay there and take that from him. You know you can always come back home. Your bedroom is still the way you left it."

Lynnette took her mother's hands in her own. "Mommie, I appreciate that you would have me, but my place is at my own house with my husband."

"But he doesn't consider his place with you. He doesn't even come home at night or talk to you when he is there. And when he does feel like communicating he talks to you like you're trash. For the life of me I don't understand why you're there. Why not stay here for a few days and let him wonder where you are for a change?"

"For as long as I can remember, you have taught me to do right by everyone, even my enemies. You haven't raised me to be a vindictive person and I thank you for that. Gerald is my husband and I love him. And as long as there is breath in my body I will continue to pray for him and our marriage. If there comes a time when I need to get away from him God will let me know. I can't make a move like that until I hear from my Heavenly Father, not my earthly mother. Do you understand what I'm saying, Mommie?"

"No, I don't understand this at all. God gave you sense, Lynnette, and you need to act like it. Don't be nobody's fool. Don't you know that this woman at church, whoever she is, is laughing at you?"

"Then let her laugh. I can't do nothing about what other people say or do, but I can control my own actions, and I want you to control yours by not letting what you now know affect your relationship with Gerald. He's still my husband and your son in-law."

Vivian took her hands from Lynnette's and looked at her as if she'd lost her mind. "How can you ask me to be nice to a man who's putting my daughter through pure hell? You can be nice and lovey-dovey if you want to, but that's you. He ain't nothing to me. I don't have to be nice. If he wants to act like a fool then I'm going to act like one right along with him."

"Mommie, please do this for me, please be nice. Don't make this situation harder than it has to be. That's why I didn't want to tell you. You can't handle stuff like this. I need you to be strong and supportive for me. Can't you move the mother role aside and be my friend?"

Vivian started to cry again.

"I just don't want you to get hurt. You're my baby and you ain't never done nothing to hurt nobody. If he doesn't want you, I want you. Come on home to Mommie. I'll take good care of you," Vivian said.

Lynnette held her mother close to her heart. "I got the best Mommie in the whole world."

She held Vivian's face and looked in her eyes. "I'm waiting for God to make a move. Either He'll separate us or bring us together. God knows I want to be happily married to Gerald. I have to stay there and keep praying that things will work out. But rest assured if God tells me to move then I'll move. But until I hear from Him and only Him, I must stay and be the wife He called me to be. This too shall pass."

Lynnette was resting on the sofa watching television when Gerald walked in from work.

"Hi, how was your day?"

Not a word from him. He walked right by Lynnette as if she wasn't there. She wanted to follow him and try to get him to talk to her, but decided to just leave him alone. She heard the shower going and wanted so badly to join him, but having him step out when she stepped in would be too humiliating. Twenty minutes later, he emerged from the bedroom dressed to kill, clean-shaven, and smelling good.

"Are you hungry? I made tuna salad."

Gerald walked by her and left the house. The clock on her night stand read three twelve A.M. when Gerald crawled into bed.

Chapter 23

"What is a marriage when there is no communication? Communication is very important. Without it, the marriage will surely fail."

Lynnette went over and over these words in her mind thinking about her last counseling session with Sheila.

"The silent treatment has gone on much too long and one of you has got to be the mature one. The longer you go without talking to each other allows Satan more time to keep you two apart."

Lynnette lay in bed listening to Gerald's breathing and turned to watch him sleep. He looked peaceful, calm, and relaxed. It was only while he was sleeping when Lynnette could at least pretend she had a good marriage, because when he rose up in the morning, hell rose up with him, and lately it wasn't just some mornings, it was every morning. But today was a new day. She was determined not to let another day go by without talking with Gerald. He is her husband and Satan must loose him and let him go today. Lynnette got out of bed and opened the blinds to let the sunshine in. This was the day the Lord had made, and she was determined to rejoice and be glad in it, come what may. She walked over to his side of the bed and kneeled to silently pray.

Good morning, Lord. Thank You for a beautiful day. I know yesterday is gone and tomorrow is not promised to arrive, so I only have today.

Gerald stirred in his sleep and mumbled something. Lynnette looked up and saw him frowning in his sleep. She continued to pray.

Lord, I'm just gonna put all the big words aside and get real with You. I've been holding some things back and I know You know my heart, so I'm just gonna say what I gotta say and get it over with. I'm sick of this crap, Jesus. I know You're probably gonna whip me real good for saying this, but

91

I gotta say it. Your word says there is nothing I can hide from You anyway, so I figured I might as well say what I'm thinking. First, I don't think it's fair I should have to go through this. I'm sorry, but I just don't. I have been praying and praying and I still can't figure out what I did that was so wrong. Yes, I know that You're God and You don't make any mistakes, but I think I might have to disagree with that. I don't do drugs or drink. I have been faithful to You my whole life. So why am I being punished? I'm serious, Lord. For the life of me I can't figure out why You would put this crazy fool in my life. Do You really expect me to keep putting up with this crap? Yes, Jesus, I said "crap" and I meant it. It just seems that Gerald gets to say and do whatever he wants, and I'm the one doing the suffering. So what are You gonna do about it? Why do You keep letting him get away with what he does? You know it ain't right, and I know it ain't right. I really want to know what was on Your mind when You took me out of eternity and placed me in my mother's womb. I was already in heaven minding my own business, and You brought me down here to go through this, and I wanna know why. You are gonna have to tell me somethin', because I don't think You're being fair. I need You, Jesus. I need You to tell me what to do. I can't do this by myself, and Gerald won't even pray with me. I can't depend on him to help this marriage heal, so it's just You and me. Please guide and strengthen me. Tell me what to say and what not to say. What kind of wife do You want me to be?

She didn't get up right away. She kept kneeling, waiting for God to answer. She wouldn't move from this spot until she heard from the Master. Lynnette thought about a time when Mount Vernon went on its women's church retreat. She and Debra decided to take the class entitled "**Lord, Teach Me To Pray**." The instructor asked the class, "How do you pray?"

A lady raised her hand. "When you pray you bow to God and ask Him for blessings."

The instructor asked, "And then what?"

"Then you get off your knees hoping and trusting that God will come through."

The instructor looked at the entire class. "Is that it?"

The young lady asked, "What else is there?"

The instructor told the class to pay close attention to what she was about to say.

"When we pray we are acknowledging that we need or desire something only God can give. But before we even open our mouths, He already knows what it is that we need or want. God said there is no good thing he will withhold from us and I truly believe that. However, as time goes on and we haven't received from God what we asked of Him, we think He hasn't come through for us, when in fact, He has. Sometimes not giving us what we ask for all the time benefits us. I believe everyone wants a good marriage. Am I right?"

Most of the class nodded their heads up and down. Others boldly said "yes."

"And there's nothing wrong with that. Who in their right mind is gonna ask for a drug addict or an abuser? I hope nobody is that crazy."

The entire class laughed at that.

"Of course we're gonna ask for a mate who will love and treat us right. But if you only kneel and make your request known to God, then get right up and go about your day thinking He is gonna give you what you want right then and there might cause a lot of heartache and pain. Sometimes we treat God like He's an order-taker at a fast food restaurant. We'll pull up to the menu board in our cars, place our order, drive around to the pick-up window, grab our food, then take off without verifying if it's the order we placed. Then we get all the way home and sit at the table ready to chow down. When you open the bag and see it's exactly what you want, that's all good. But what happens when you get all the way home, get undressed, sit at the table, and open the bag to see white meat when you ordered dark meat? What if you got Dr. Pepper cola instead of Pepsi cola? What do you do then? Truth be told, some of us would be ready to cuss. And if we have nothing in our stomach but that morning's yogurt, then get home nice and comfy on the sofa only to find out we got the wrong order, some of us would be ready to cut somebody."

The class broke out laughing because they knew she was telling the truth.

"Come on now. Tell the truth and stay in church. I'm talkin' about having a tall AT-TEE-TUDE. And don't let us drive crazy trying to get home to see *Dallas* or *Knots Landing*. We would be hotter than Louisiana's Hot Sauce, wouldn't we?"

There were a bunch of Amens to that.

"But what if we had taken the time to check our order to make absolutely sure it's the right one? Then we would have seen that what we accepted wasn't the right order. So what do we do? Are we gonna get dressed again and risk missing *Dallas* to go all the way across town to return the order? Heck no. We're gonna sit right there on that sofa and say **'it ain't what I ordered, but it's gonna have to do for now 'cause I'm hungry and I gotta find out who shot J.R. Ewing.'**

We're disappointed, but hey, chicken is chicken. So we sit there and eat that dry breast as long as it eases the hunger pain. And an hour later we're hungry again because the chicken breast wasn't fulfilling. Now we're looking for something else to fill the void in our stomachs. See, the chicken breast was tasty, but it didn't satisfy us. Now we're searching for something else to satisfy what the right order would have had we taken the time to verify and make sure we got what we asked for and not settled for just anything. Sometimes when we get off our knees quick, fast, and in a hurry, we take for granted that God is going to give us what we asked for immediately. And when we have that type of attitude, we accept the first thing that comes along that looks or smells good. Go ahead and tell God what it is you want, but ask for patience as well, and learn how to wait and make sure you hear His voice and not your own. He answers all of our prayers, but sometimes we make the mistake of thinking we hear a **'yes'** from God when He clearly says **'no'** or **'wait.'** Be sure what you're asking for is in His will. We'll ask God for a saved Christian man, but if we don't **'wait'** for God to bless us in His own time, we'll fall for the first half-way decent man that pays us some attention, thinking he must be sent from God. And a few months later or after marriage, we find out this man has three more wives in other states, or we may see his face one night on *America's Most Wanted* for murder."

The class really thought that was funny.

"See, you all are laughing, but it's true. We have got to know and realize when God says **'no'** or **'wait.'** So when you're down on your knees praying, don't just jump up and go. Stay there and meditate and wait to hear from God. And know this, He's an on-time God, not a right-now God."

Lynnette wished she'd recognized God's voice in time when He told her to wait. What had she gotten herself into? She was still kneeling when Jesus spoke to her.

"LOVE YOUR HUSBAND."

She asked Him silently. *How can I love him when he won't speak to me and treats me so bad?*

"YOU ASKED ME TO HELP YOU, YET YOU QUESTION MY ANSWER?"

Lord, I don't mean to be disrespectful. I truly believe You know what's best for me and I know whatever it is You tell me to do is right. I just ask You to give me the tools I need to do Your will.

"WHEN YOU WERE BAPTIZED IN MY NAME YOU RECEIVED THE GIFT OF THE HOLY GHOST. LEARN TO USE YOUR GIFT I'VE ALREADY GIVEN YOU. THE HOLY GHOST IS THE ONLY TOOL YOU NEED. REMEMBER THAT I AM WITH YOU ALWAYS."

Yes, Lord, I know that you are with me everyday, but how can I love him when he rejects everything I try to do? He won't talk to me or pray with me. It's hard to love him when he ignores every attempt I make to set things right between us. I speak, he doesn't speak. I smile, he frowns. I ask him to pray with me, he tells me he doesn't feel like praying. So what am I to do?

"LEAVE HIM ALONE. I HAVE ALLOWED HIM TO EXPERI-
ENCE A SPIRITUAL WARFARE. DURING THIS TIME IT WILL
SEEM AS THOUGH YOU'RE HIS WORST ENEMY. DON'T
FRET, FOR I HAVE FULL CONTROL OF THE SITUATION.
DON'T PRESSURE HIM OR TRY TO FORCE HIM TO DO ANY-
THING. YOU WILL ONLY HURT YOURSELF IF YOU INTER-
FERE. KNOW THAT I AM GOD. YOU MUST TRUST THAT I
AND I ALONE WILL MAKE EVERYTHING ALRIGHT. LEAVE
YOUR BURDENS IN MY HANDS AND BELIEVE MY WORD IS
TRUE. IF YOU TRUST ME I WILL WORK EVERYTHING OUT
FOR YOUR GOOD, EVEN THOUGH YOU CAN'T SEE THAT
NOW. LEARN TO LOOK AT THINGS WITH YOUR SPIRITUAL
EYE. YOU MUST SEE THINGS AS I SEE THEM. LOVE YOUR
HUSBAND JUST AS I HAVE COMMANDED."

Lynnette wiped the tears from her eyes then stood up and looked at
her sleeping husband who was still frowning. She kissed him lightly on his
forehead then turned to walk to the kitchen. It was Saturday and Lynnette
was going to wake her husband up with a wonderful breakfast in bed...or
so she thought.

Push

Pressing is pushing. When you commit to bring forth all that God has for you, you may have to push against everything anybody ever did to you or said about you. You may have to battle years of suppression, oppression and depression. You may have to push with all your might to release the treasure God has put within you, but He wants to bring it to birth. He put the treasure there. He'll help you bring the treasure out. But it is up to you to push. In fact, it may not happen if you don't!

But what do you push against? You don't push against other people. This isn't a battle in the natural. It is a battle in the spirit. You have to push against the opposition of the devil in its many forms. His opposition attacks you in subtle, but debilitating ways, such as bad memories, low self-esteem, or feelings of unworthiness. The devil may have spent years pushing you aside, pulling you back, and putting you down. But now the Lord says to you, "I want to open you up. I want you to give birth to that which I put in you."

It is time to say to yourself and to the world, "It's my turn to conceive. It's time for the treasure that God put inside me to come forth. It's time for me to be loosed to do what God created me to do."

When a baby is born, everything in the family changes. The same is true for you. When you give birth to the treasure God has put in you, everything around you will be different-your marriage, your relationship with your children, your place in your church, your neighborhood, and your workplace. God's blessing is an overflowing blessing, and it touches every area of your life.

Every woman knows when she is pregnant. In fact, a woman often has an inner knowing long before she feels the baby moving inside her womb. The same is true in the spiritual realm. I'm talking about giving birth to the gifts and talents and powers and the ministries of the Holy Spirit inside you. I don't know what specific thing God wants to birth in you, but you do. Like an expectant mother, you have a knowing deep inside.

Don't fail today to give birth to what God put in you. Now is the time for the baby-that treasure-to be born. Go for it. Push!

Chapter 24

Keep your tongue from evil, And your lips from speaking deceit. Psalms 34:13

Lynnette was feeling good. The sun was shining bright and her husband came home last night. These were two good reasons why she was in the kitchen singing and cooking. While standing at the stove scrambling eggs she had no idea she was being watched. She turned to go into the dining room to get a breakfast tray when she saw Gerald standing at the kitchen door. She was disappointed that he was awake already, because she wanted to surprise him with breakfast in bed. She opened her mouth to say good morning, but his words came out faster.

"Why are you making so much noise?"

For a moment she was at a loss for words. She had hoped he would be pleased to have breakfast in bed, but at the sound of his voice, she knew right then this was another morning the enemy had stolen. By the angry look on his face, she could tell once again Gerald had gotten up on the wrong side of the bed, and whatever his reason for being in such a foul mood would somehow, someway, turn out to be her fault. That's just the way it was.

"I was going to wake you with breakfast in bed," Lynnette said.

"Did I ask you to cook anything for me?"

Lynnette was stunned. "No, uh, I just thought it would be nice to...."

Before she could finish her sentence, he turned and walked back to the bedroom. She sat down at the kitchen table and looked at the food she cooked. She would have to throw it all away, because she knew she wouldn't be able to keep it down. She heard what sounded like doors shutting, went in the bedroom, and saw him opening and closing dresser drawers.

"What are you looking for?"

Gerald didn't answer her, didn't even acknowledge her existence. He would slide one drawer open and rumble through socks and underwear that Lynnette had taken time to fold neatly, then slam the drawer shut and go to the next drawer and repeat the process.

"What are you looking for, Honey?"

He had taken every dark-colored sock out of the drawer and thrown them to the floor. "Where are my navy socks?"

"Sweetie, you wore those socks with your navy shirt and slacks last Friday night when you went out. I guess they must still be in the dirty clothes hamper. Where are you going so early on a Saturday morning?"

He settled for a pair of black nylon socks instead, then walked over to the closet to put on his white shirt. "If you just have to know my every move, I'm going to a funeral."

"Whose funeral is it?"

"One of my friend's sister died and her funeral is today."

"What friend, Gerald?"

He stopped tying his tie and looked at Lynnette.

"You don't know the friend, so don't worry about it. Why are you asking me so many questions? Why don't you answer some questions for a change? What did you eat yesterday? How many pounds have you lost this week? Did you get an abortion yet? And when are you going to wash the clothes? It's because of you that I can't even wear what I had planned to wear today."

Lynnette walked up to him and stood in his face. "Look, I work forty hours a week just like you do. Okay? You know I do the laundry every two weeks and this is not a wash week. You put those socks in the hamper, not me. If you knew you wanted to wear them today you should have washed them yourself. And as far as an abortion goes, I won't even entertain that thought."

She walked out of the bedroom and into the bathroom, but before she could close the door Gerald was on her heels. "You see, that's what I'm talking about. I was just telling a friend the other day what I had to deal with at home and they advised me to leave you if I'm not happy. They said it's no use staying in a marriage if we can't talk to each other."

"You know what, Gerald? You can do whatever you wanna do. You always have and you always will. But you better be careful of the company you keep and the ungodly counsel you get from the streets. Whoever this friend is who's telling you to leave your wife can't possibly be saved. Don't you know that the devil places certain people in your life to destroy you? And it's not that I don't wanna talk to you. You are the one who does not wanna talk to me. I'm always the one initiating the conversation. I ask you how your day was or how you're feeling. You don't even respond when I say good morning or good night."

"I don't respond because I really don't want to hear your voice. I have a good day when I don't have to talk to you or see your face."

That remark threw Lynnette. It threw her heart, mind, and soul. She had been so strong until then. Counseling had taught her to stand strong through verbal abuse. Sheila warned her that the enemy can slice and dice, so she would have to be ready when he took out the knife. But she wasn't ready for this. She felt faint like she was going to fall, so she backed herself up and leaned on the sink. She didn't even know she was crying until a tear dripped from her chin and splashed onto her toes. Lately she had been good at hiding her emotions from Gerald. She never let him see her cry anymore. She didn't want to give him the satisfaction. But today was a different story. She would have given anything for him to have hit her instead of allowing those words to come out of his mouth. Eventually, bruises and wounds will heal, but these words will stay with her forever. She stood there with a tear-soaked face, looked at her husband, and saw that his eyes were the color of blood.

"I don't care about you crying, your tears don't move me. You think just because you're crying I'm supposed to apologize? Well that's too bad because I'm not sorry for how I feel. You make me sick. I don't want to be around you, and the sound of your voice makes my stomach turn. That's why I don't come home at night sometimes. I don't wanna smell your perfume. I don't wanna see any pictures of your family, and I don't want to lay in bed next to you. And that strawberry stuff is starting to stink. I asked you to do one thing for me, just one thing, and you couldn't even do that. We wouldn't have to go through this if you would just lose some weight. You are not a wife. You don't know how to be a wife. To me, you are nothing. You will never be anything, and I wish I had never married you, because the sight of you makes me wanna throw up."

Lynnette was flabbergasted. How in the world could a man, saved or not, fix his mouth to say those words to his wife? All of a sudden, she felt like she had the flu. She was chilled to the bone, yet she was burning up.

"You are an evil and hateful man, Gerald Hawkins. You're a liar and a cheater and the love of God ain't in you."

"Yeah, I'm all that, but you married me and you're the one who don't want a divorce. Now you tell me who's the fool."

Gerald went back into the bedroom, grabbed his suit jacket from the closet, and walked out the front door.

Lynnette felt like he had physically tore into her chest, snatched her heart out, thrown it to the floor, and stepped on it. She was spiritually and emotionally drained. She had reached her limit. It was impossible to love Gerald anymore. She decided if he wanted out of the marriage, she would no longer try and hold on to him. God is just going to have to understand that she couldn't continue to set herself up to be mentally beaten anymore. She walked back into the bedroom, kneeled by the bed, and told God exactly how she felt.

"Lord, You know I've tried to work things out with Gerald. I've done everything You told me to do. I can't go on like this. I place my husband in Your hands. I don't know what else to do. Since he wants out, then I pray You will give him what he wants, because I can't deal with it anymore. I love Gerald and You know I do, but it's time for me to love Lynnette. I pray You will cover him in Your blood and keep him out of harm's way."

Lynnette's eyes were heavy from crying. She refolded the clothes Gerald had thrown to the floor and placed them neatly in the drawers again. She went into the kitchen, got a bottle of Crisco oil from the cabinet, and prayed over it. Then she walked into the bathroom, got a cotton swab from the medicine chest, opened the bottle, and dipped the swab into the oil. Then she wiped the sink faucet with the swab, then wiped the toilet handle and the towel rack. She dipped the swab in the oil again, then wiped the bottle of lotion, the soap dish, the tube of toothpaste, and every bottle of his cologne. On the way out of the bathroom, she dipped the swab in the oil again and wiped the light switch and both doorknobs.

"Satan, I rebuke you in the name of Jesus."

She walked to the kitchen and wiped the swab over each knob on the stove, then she wiped the door handle to the refrigerator.

"You no longer have any power over my marriage."

She dipped the swab again and wiped every drawer handle and every cabinet knob. She opened the cabinets and wiped every plate and glass, then opened the drawers and wiped every knife, fork, and spoon.

"Jesus is the head of this house."

She dipped the swab again and wiped every cereal box and every canned good. She wiped the bags of flour and sugar. She opened the refrigerator and dipped the swab again. She wiped the carton of orange juice, the bottle of drinking water, and the pitcher of Kool-Aid drink.

"I claim victory in Jesus' name."

Lynnette couldn't stop. She was out of control. She dipped the swab again and wiped every egg, the packages of cheese, and lunch meat. She wiped the jars of mayonnaise and sandwich spread. She wiped every apple and orange. She took her time to wipe every grape, hoping that whatever Gerald ate, he would swallow the Holy Ghost along with it. She dipped the swab again and opened the freezer.

"Hallelujah, glory to You, Lord."

She wiped the box of popsicles, the box of waffles, and every package of frozen meat. She took out the ice trays and dabbed every cube. She went into the dining room and wiped the table and each chair. She pulled out a chair, stepped onto it, and reached up and dabbed the two strings attached to the ceiling fan. One for the light and the other for the fan. She got down and walked into the living room and dipped the swab again.

"Fill this house with Your presence, Lord."

She wiped the sofa and love seat. She wiped the T.V., video cassette recorder, remote control, and the stereo system. She walked into the bedroom and dipped the swab again. She wiped every dresser drawer. She went to the closet and opened the door and dabbed every one of Gerald's suit jackets. She dabbed every shirt and tie. She dabbed every pair of pants. She went to the dresser and pulled out each drawer and went through them all. She dabbed every T-shirt, brief, boxer short, and sock. She dipped the swab, walked over to his side of the bed, and dabbed his pillow. Then she went back to the closet and dabbed every one of his shoes. She walked into his office and looked at his desk.

"I plead the blood of Jesus in my house."

She dipped the swab and wiped his computer and keyboard. She wiped the mouse pad and every book on his desk. Then she turned around and wiped his free weights and exercise bench.

Having done all that, Lynnette threw the swab in the garbage can and put what was left of the Crisco oil back in the kitchen cabinet. She then walked to the front door, opened it wide, and yelled, "Satan, in the name Jesus I'm serving notice to you. You've got to go, so get the hell out of my house."

She slammed the door so hard it almost came off its hinges.

The telephone rang and she hoped it was Debra or Sheila because she really needed to talk.

"Hello?"

"Hello, is this Lynnette?"

She frowned at the unfamiliar voice. "Yes, this is Lynnette. Who's calling?"

"Lynnette, this is Dawn Roberts from the choir. Did I catch you at a bad time?"

"Oh hi, Dawn. I'm sorry but I didn't recognize your voice. How are you?"

"I'm wonderful, thanks for asking. I'm glad I caught you before you went about your day. I was wondering if you could do a huge favor for me today."

"Sure, Dawn, I'll help if I can. What is it?"

"My cousin's wedding is this afternoon and her soloist suddenly came down with the flu. She called this morning asking if I could get the choir to sing, but it's simply not enough time to get everybody together. Since I was so impressed with your voice on Thursday night, I thought I'd call and see if you're available to sing today."

In all honesty Lynnette wanted to decline. All she wanted to do was lie on the sofa all day. Then she thought about the promise she made to Debra one day at the beauty shop.

"I want you to promise me that no matter what happens in your life you will keep singing to the glory of God, because He's worthy. Okay?"

"Okay, Debra, I promise."

"Thanks a lot, Debra." Lynnette was deep in thought and hadn't realized that she'd spoken out loud.

"Pardon me, what did you say, Lynnette?"

"Uh, I'll be happy to do it for you, Dawn. Is there a special song I should learn right quick?"

"I think what you sang in choir rehearsal is an excellent song. Those words of love and dedication are perfect for the occasion. You will be singing as the bridal party walks down the aisle and take their places up front.

Dawn told her the time and location of the wedding and thanked her twice before hanging up.

Lynnette had a problem. The song she sang at choir rehearsal was not a song she heard on the radio or heard anyone else sing. When she got to choir rehearsal, she didn't know what she was going to sing. It was when she got to the microphone that she opened herself up to God and the words flowed freely. She sang the words as they came into her heart. That song was her personal testimony, and right now she couldn't even remember the first words she sang.

The organist asked Lynnette what song was she going to sing, and she was honest when she told him she didn't know. But as usual God came through for her. She calmly walked up to the microphone, asked God to write on her tongue, and He did exactly that. As she started to sing, the organist joined in and tried to follow her but had a hard time because she was flowing in her own way. He decided to stop playing because Lynnette's voice carried its own music. She didn't need help from an organ. When Lynnette finished the song, she opened her eyes and saw that the bridal party were all lined up at the front of the church and the guests were on their feet applauding. Even the bride, who wasn't supposed to be seen yet, was peeking her head into the sanctuary. After the ceremony, the happy couple walked over to Lynnette and invited her to the reception. She declined the offer, but told them that she was glad she could help them out on their special day. They thanked her and placed two hundred and fifty dollars cash in her hand. The bride told her she sang a beautiful song and asked where had she heard it before. Lynnette told her she'd never heard it before today.

Get Emotional About It

We must understand the difference between our spirits and our emotions. They are linked, yet they are separate. In our spirits, we have God-consciousness. The spirit realm is the realm in which we relate to God intimately and fully. In our bodies, we have world-consciousness, an awareness of our physical world. In our souls, we have self-consciousness. Our emotions are part of our soul realm.

To tell a person not to be emotional is to tell a person not to be human. It is to deny that person's God-given right and privilege to enter into full relationship with the Creator. It is to deny the soul realm. Don't ever try to tell me that God doesn't care about how I feel. I know He does.

Because of the uniqueness of a woman's femininity and her ability to express emotions, there were times in history that God specifically called for women. For example, Jeremiah said, "Send for skillful wailing women, that they may come" (Jeremiah 9:17). God wanted to see tears and brokenness on the altar. He wanted to hear expressions of sorrow over the fact that His people were being carried away into bondage. He said, "Find Me some women and tell them to weep."

God knows the power of tears, of feelings. Jesus said about prayer, "Whatever things you ask when you pray, believe that you receive them, and you will have them" (Mark 11:24). When you desire something, you don't just "want" it. To desire something is to want it with passion. Jesus said, "Make known to Me the things you can't do without, the things you want passionately."

Man looks on the outward appearance, but God looks on the heart. He is looking to see what we desire with all of our hearts, not to see the whims or fleeting ideas of our minds. Is there something today that you want so much you are willing to lie on the altar and cry for it? Is there a desire to see God move in your life—a desire that burns in your innermost being with such passion that you can't forget it, can't escape it, can't dismiss it, and can't ignore it? Is there something you want so desperately to see God do that you wake up in the middle of the night thinking about it? Is there something you feel so certain God wants to do and will do that you just know it is going to be done? Are you convinced, even when everything around you says otherwise?

That is your desire. It arises from your spirit, and it's meant to be expressed by your soul. God expects you to get emotional about it!

Chapter 25

The righteousness cry out, and the Lord hears, And delivers them out of all their troubles. The Lord is near to those who have a broken heart, And saves such as have a contrite spirit. Many are the afflictions of the righteous, But the Lord delivers him out of them all. He guards all his bones; Not one of them is broken. Evil shall slay the wicked, And those who hate the righteous shall be condemned. The Lord redeems the soul of His servants, And none of those who trust in Him shall be condemned. Psalms 34:17-22

It seemed like Lynnette just couldn't get home fast enough. She got caught at every stop light since she left the wedding. Still upset and bothered by Gerald's hateful words, she just wanted to go home, soak in the tub, and rest. It was bad enough she had to miss her hair appointment because of the wedding, but playing "stop and go" at every other corner was bringing on fatigue. She was ready to go right through a yellow light, at the corner of Homan Avenue and Roosevelt Road but she spotted a police car and decided she would have to sit this one out too. A young man drove up in a brand new black BMW convertible on her right. He looked her way and smiled. Lynnette smiled back at him, but quickly turned her head and looked the other way. *Ooh, he is too cute.*

"Hey, Cutie, how are you doing?"

Lynnette looked at him again and saw that he was looking her way. She looked to her left to see if maybe he was looking through her car and talking to someone else, but no one was there.

Oh my God, he's talking to me.

"Cat got your tongue or are you just evil today?"

Lynnette didn't know what to do or say. This had never happened to her before, but she had to say something or he would think she was snobbish.

104

"I'm fine thank you."

"I didn't ask how you are looking. Anybody in their right mind can see you're fine. I wanna know how you're feeling."

Oh my God, Lord Jesus, what is going on here, and what is taking this light so long to change?

"I'm feeling good, thanks for asking."

"My name is Jasper. What's yours?"

Lynnette looked at this man who was smiling at her. His smile reminded her of the yellow smiley face stickers she use to get in grammar school for getting a good grade on her spelling test.

Man, he's got some pretty teeth.

"My name is Lynnette. It's nice to meet you, Jasper."

"Is it? Then pull over so I can show you how nice I can be."

Lynnette's heart was pumping overtime, and for one second she actually considered doing what he asked. It would be nice for a man to talk to her like she's worth something. He almost had her until she glanced down at her hand on her lap and saw her wedding ring. She held it up for him to see. "Sorry, Jasper, I'm married. No can do."

"Happily?"

"No, I can't say I am, but I'm still married nonetheless. It wouldn't be right."

Jasper looked at her as if she'd broken his heart. "Are you sure? I would treat you real good and there's nothing I wouldn't give you."

Sold. That's all he had to say. "Okay, pull over."

The light changed, Jasper turned right, and Lynnette put her right turn signal on and started making her way into the right lane to follow him.

"WHAT ARE YOU DOING MY DAUGHTER?"

Lynnette quickly stepped on the gas and went straight ahead. In the rearview mirror she saw Jasper standing outside his car door looking at her car speed down the street.

"I'm sorry, Lord. I'm so sorry, Jesus, please forgive me. Oh God, I'm so sorry. I promise I won't do that again. I'm sorry, Lord, I'm sorry, I'm sorry, I'm sorry."

Lynnette parked her car in the driveway next to Gerald's. This was one of those times when she hoped he wouldn't be home. It was about six forty-five on a Saturday evening and she thought she wouldn't see him again until Monday or Tuesday. She thought about Jasper and her heart started to race. She stood on the front porch, took a deep breath, dismissed all thoughts of Jasper, and turned the key in the lock and went inside. The stereo was on the jazz station playing softly. On the cocktail table were two champagne glasses, both half empty. Next to them was a champagne bottle, completely empty. Sitting on the sofa in shock were Gerald and a woman who looked familiar to Lynnette. From that point on, everything went in slow motion. Gerald was the first to move as he got up and came toward Lynnette. She couldn't take her eyes off this woman who was in *her* house, sitting on *her* sofa, drinking *her* champagne from *her* glass, listening to *her* stereo with *her* husband. Suddenly she remembered choir rehearsal. Everyone was applauding her on her song except this woman. And she wasn't too happy when Lynnette sat next to her. Then she remembered Gerald's telephone conversation.

"I can't stop her from joining the choir, Simone."

Simone. That's her name, Simone.

Gerald walked over to Lynnette. "It's not what it looks like."

Lynnette balled up her fist and hit Gerald across his nose so hard it felt like she had broken her hand. He lost his balance and fell backward unto the floor. Then Lynnette jumped over the cocktail table and leapt on top of Simone. It happened so fast, Simone didn't even see her coming. Lynnette was swinging and punching. Simone tried with all of her might to move out from under Lynnette, but to no avail. It was Simone's scream that brought Gerald back into consciousness. He stood up and dizzily made his way over to the sofa. He couldn't see Simone at all, Lynnette was crushing her. Simone screamed again.

"Gerald, get her off of me!"

He grabbed Lynnette's legs and started to pull, but lost his grip and fell back into the stereo, and it came crashing to the floor. Gerald's head hit the wall so hard he actually forgot his name for a few minutes. By now both Simone and Lynnette were rolling on the floor. Somehow, Simone got away from Lynnette and tried to run away from her, but Lynnette was too quick. She grabbed Simone by the left ankle and held on. Simone lost her balance and fell on her face which caused her to break her nose and two front teeth. Simone screamed out in pain which awakened Gerald again. He leapt on top of Lynnette and tried with all of his might to pull her off of Simone but couldn't do it. Simone was on her knees trying to crawl out of Lynnette's grip but Lynnette wasn't having it. She held on to Simone like red stripes on a candy cane. She wanted to wrap her big self around Simone's little self and squeeze the life out of her.

Gerald's face was bloody. He was half out of his mind and out of breath. He was pulling Lynnette's ankles and she was pulling Simone's ankles. Lynnette kicked backward and struck Gerald right on the tip of his chin which caused his bottom teeth to clash with his top teeth, and three of them cracked and fell out of his mouth. Gerald was no match for Lynnette, but again, he leapt on top of her and started to pull her off of Simone. Lynnette lost her grip again and Simone ran through the kitchen and out the back door.

The front door flew open and three police officers ran in, pulled Gerald off of Lynnette, and handcuffed him. Two officers helped Lynnette up and asked her what happened. She explained how she came home and found her husband and a woman in her house, and things got ugly from there.

In the end, Gerald was arrested for assault and battery because he was on top of Lynnette when the police arrived. Lynnette asked if Simone could be arrested for trespassing, and they informed her she wasn't trespassing because Gerald had invited her into their home.

After the police left, Lynnette had time to look at her house. The living room looked like a tornado hit it. She went to the linen closet to get some towels to clean up Simone's and Gerald's teeth and blood when she saw all of her pictures on the closet floor. Pictures of their wedding, pictures of her family, and pictures of her and Gerald together were all on the floor of the closet. Lynnette walked back into the living room and noticed that not one picture that involved her face or anyone in her family was hanging. In the bathroom she saw that all of her toiletries were placed under the bathroom sink. A song came to mind and she started to cry and sing as she asked God to direct her from this moment.

"What shall I do? What path do I take now? My Lord, my Saviour, tell me where do I go from here?"

In the bathroom, she placed her toothbrush and toiletries back in their places.

"I feel so alone in this world. I need You to tell me what to do. I'm waiting on You, Lord."

She went into the living room and sat down on the love seat and looked at the two champagne glasses.

"I know You have an answer for me, You alone can set me free."

She began to rehang every picture of her parents and the pictures of her and Gerald.

"I can't go on without Your guidance, I'm too weak to do this by myself. Lord, please walk with me."

When she got to their wedding picture, she found that she couldn't hang it up. She took the picture, sat down on the chair, and held the picture close to her heart.

"In Your bosom, Lord, is where I long to be. No one else can do for me what You can. You're my Prince of Peace and my King, Lord, You're my everything."

Lynnette stood and removed all the pictures she just hung. She was crying so hard she could hardly see what she was doing. She put the pictures back on the floor of the closet, then went into the bedroom and kneeled by the bed still crying and singing to God.

"I give You praise, glory, and honor. I bow down to You and acknowledge You as my personal Saviour. I lay at Your feet and surrender my soul to You, Lord. Please mend my broken heart as only You can. I put

my trust in no man. Give me my life back. Give me my joy back. Give me my praise back. Give me my peace back. Give me my hope back. I'm tired of living with this misery and strife. I want to laugh again, sing again, jump and shout again, dance again. I want to praise Your name with fire in my heart like I used to. And Lord, I'm sorry. I'm sorry for falling out of love with You and allowing Gerald to take Your place in my life. I've put him before You, Jesus, and I beg You to forgive me."

Lynnette was so emotional and deep in her praise that no one else in the world existed. It was just her and her God.

"I'm sorry for ignoring You, I love You, Jesus, sorry for disobeying You, I love you, Jesus, sorry for not trusting You, I love You, Jesus. Please forgive me, I love You, Jesus, please accept me back, I love You, Jesus. I need You, exalt You, magnify You, praise You, glorify You, adore You, want You, and I love You. Your joy is my strength. You are my Healer, my Deliverer. You're the One who wakes me in the morning and keeps me from day to day. I love You and I bless You. I bow down to You, Lord and I'm going to stay right here until I hear from You. So please tell me what to do. Where do I go from here?"

Lynnette stayed on her knees all night waiting to hear from God. She was not going to get up from that spot until He spoke to her. She needed answers and she needed them like yesterday. She would stay put until she was caught up in the air if she had to. It was three forty eight A.M. when the Holy Spirit came into her presence and told Lynnette what she needed to do. It also told her to put on the whole armor of God because the worst was yet to come.

Chapter 26

On Sunday morning, Lynnette lay in bed and wondered if she should go to church. She was twelve weeks pregnant and still nauseated in the mornings. Finally she forced herself to shower and get ready for church. She knew she needed to hear some preaching today.

Neither Gerald or Simone were present. During testimonial period Lynnette stood up and told the whole congregation what happened in her home the night before. She stated her name as well as Gerald and Simone's names. The look on the choir's face was horrifying. After saying what she had to say, Lynnette walked out of the choir stand and out of the church as everyone watched. She knew she would never see the inside of True Divine Baptist Church again.

Chapter 27

By the following Wednesday, Lynnette was in her new apartment in Brookfield, Illinois just outside of Chicago, in one of the west suburbs. After seeing Simone in her house, Lynnette thought the place was dirty. She knew she could never sit on that sofa again. Having seen all of her pictures and toiletries removed made Lynnette feel as though she had died and was a ghost looking down on Gerald and his new life. Maybe she was the one trespassing, not Simone. Obviously Gerald wanted Simone there so she decided to let them have the house. Dawn called Lynnette and told her how sorry she was to see her go and that the choir was truly missing out on a beautiful voice. She also told Lynnette that Pastor Vaughn removed Simone from the choir, and she would not be allowed to sing or serve in any church activity until she completed a thirteen-week course on "Marriage And The Family" and the same rule applied to Gerald. After much begging and pleading for Lynnette to come back, Dawn wished her well. Lynnette told Dawn God was taking her in another direction.

On Friday evening, Vivian, Debra, Betty, Sheila, and to Lynnette's surprise, Thelma, gathered at her new apartment for a house-warming. Lynnette told them that if they wanted to bring things for the apartment, it would be okay. However, she was not celebrating the fact that she had left her husband. But Vivian didn't care what Lynnette said. She brought balloons, party favors, and a cake that read "Goodbye Yesterday, Hello Tomorrow." Lynnette told Vivian she didn't want any cake because this wasn't a party, but when Thelma cut the cake and big, red, juicy strawberries fell out from between the layers, Lynnette couldn't help herself. She had two pieces. Thelma walked over to her, hugged her tight, and told her she was glad when she called and told her what happened and that she had moved out.

"No matter what happens you will always be my daughter in-law," Thelma said.

"It's very important to me that you know I truly loved your son. And I still do love him, but I couldn't allow him to keep walking all over me," Lynnette said.

Thelma covered Lynnette's mouth with her hand. "You don't have to justify yourself to me or any one else. I know you were good to him. David and I never questioned that. Gerald has always done what he wanted to do, no matter who got hurt in the process. He came by today with his mouth looking like piano keys. Every other tooth was missing. He looked pitiful. David told him he wasn't raised to treat women this way and he's still not welcomed in our home until he gets himself together. At this point, Lynnette, all we can do is pray for him. He's in God's hands now. I was surprised to hear you dropped the charges against him, because I wouldn't have."

Betty fried some catfish, Debra made cole slaw, Vivian made spaghetti, Sheila made garlic bread, and Thelma made some Kool-Aid drink. The ladies laughed and had a good time as they turned on some music and made a "soul-train" line in the living room and danced. It was ladies night and the feeling was just right.

Chapter 28

Two weeks later, Lynnette was standing at the kitchen counter. She was finishing a cup of coffee and just about to leave for work when the doorbell rang. She glanced at her watch. It was thirteen minutes after seven. It was too early for the Jehovah's Witnesses and she wasn't expecting anyone, certainly not this early in the morning on a week day. She walked into the living room and looked outside. She didn't recognize any cars. She assumed whoever it was must've rang her bell by mistake. She stood there looking out the window waiting for the person to either walk away or ring the bell for the people downstairs. Then she remembered Mr. and Mrs. Hamilton moved out last weekend. There was no one in the two-flat building but her. She was on the second floor, so she couldn't see who was ringing the bell. Her watch read sixteen minutes after seven. If she wanted to be at work at seven thirty she would have to leave now. The doorbell rang again. She walked to her door, opened it, and yelled downstairs.

"Yes, who is it?"

"It's the Cook County Sheriff's Department. I'm looking for Mrs. Lynnette Hawkins."

Lynnette went down to the door and looked through the peep hole. Outside stood a tall white man with dark sunglasses. Because she lived in the building alone, she didn't want to open the door for just anyone.

"Can I see some identification please?" she asked.

The man reached into his shirt pocket for his I.D. card and held it up to the peep hole for Lynnette to see. She read the card which said, "**Jason Welch, Cook County Sheriff's Department.**" He kindly removed his sunglasses so she could compare his picture with the real thing. She unlocked the bottom lock but didn't removed the chain. When the door opened, he moved in closer.

"Are you Lynnette Hawkins?"

She hesitated. "Yes, how can I help you?"

The man reached inside his briefcase and presented her with a legal sized envelope with a green label on the front. "I have a certified letter for you. Please sign here."

At that moment she knew what was in the envelope and didn't want to sign anything, but knew she had to. Through the small opening of the door, he gave her the envelope and an ink pen. She took the envelope from the man and looked at it.

Could this really be happening?

Lynnette hadn't realized that she was crying until the man spoke to her. "I'm sorry, Miss, but I need you to sign the card please."

With shaking hands she signed the card and gave it and the ink pen back to him.

"Miss, you have twenty-one days to respond to this letter. Thank you and have a good day."

She closed the door and slowly walked back upstairs staring at the letter. In her apartment, she sat at the dining room table and opened it.

"Petition to Dissolve Marriage, Gerald Hawkins vs. Lynnette Hawkins."

She looked to the bottom of the paper for the grounds of divorce.

"EXTREME AND REPEATED MENTAL CRUELTY AGAINST THE PETITIONER."

She fainted and fell out of the chair.

Chapter 29

Ever since Vivian found out about Lynnette and Gerald, she called Lynnette at least twice a day just to make sure she was alright. Vivian knew her baby girl was strong and able to take care of herself, but she couldn't help but feel the pain her daughter was going through. Lynnette wasn't the only one who cried herself to sleep at night. Vivian shared her sorrows, and she too had awakened many mornings with her eyelids swollen and sealed together by dried tears. Vivian had pleaded with Lynnette to move in with her and Walter, but Lynnette thought moving back home was taking a step backward in life. Lynnette wanted privacy. She knew her parents meant well and loved her very much, but she didn't think she could handle them, especially her mother being overprotective. She thanked God for having such loyal and caring parents, but she could only imagine what it would be like living under the same roof with them. She would constantly be asked if she was alright or needed anything. She needed her own space. This way if she didn't want to be bothered, she didn't have to answer the door or the telephone.

Vivian let the telephone ring about twenty-five times before she hung up and called again. She did this about three times, then she called Lynnette's extension at work. She got her voice mail and left eight messages. It wasn't like Lynnette not to return her mother's calls, because she knew if Vivian didn't hear her voice every four hours, she would totally freak out. Lynnette's voice message didn't say she was in a meeting or out of the office today, so Vivian assumed she was busy. But how busy could she be that she couldn't return one phone call?

After she left the last message on Lynnette's voicemail Vivian pressed zero and asked the operator to put her through to Betty's extension. The operator transferred Vivian to Betty's line and Vivian told her it was urgent that she speak with Lynnette. Betty explained to Vivian that Lynnette had not come to work. Betty had also been calling her apartment. She told Vivian Lynnette had been stressed and she assumed Lynnette had taken the day off to rest, but it wasn't like her not to call in. After Lynnette was more than an hour late and hadn't called she became concerned and called Lynnette's apartment and hadn't got an answer. Vivian apologized for disturbing Betty and promised to have Lynnette call her as soon as she'd spoken with her.

Vivian hung up with Betty and quickly called Walter at work. She told him Lynnette hadn't shown up to work, no one has heard from her, and she'd called the apartment many times without getting an answer. Walter told Vivian maybe Lynnette just wanted to be left alone for a while. He knew how much Vivian called her and it even got on his nerves, but he couldn't tell Vivian because she wouldn't understand. He once told Vivian she called Lynnette too much and maybe if she didn't smother her all the time, Lynnette wouldn't be so depressed. Vivian told him Lynnette was her baby and it was she who carried her for nine months, not him. She told him she knew when her baby needed her and no matter what he said, she was taking the spare keys Lynnette had given her and going over to the apartment, and if he cared for Lynnette, he would meet her there as soon as possible. Walter had to admit it wasn't like Lynnette not to call in to work, so he agreed to meet Vivian at the apartment. When Vivian drove up, Walter was already standing on the front porch. Vivian got out of the car and ran up to the door, keys ready.

"Walter, her car is still here. Did you ring the bell?"

"Yeah, but she didn't answer."

When they entered the apartment, Vivian called for Lynnette, but didn't get an answer. They walked through the living room into the dining room, and saw Lynnette lying on the floor. The chair she had been sitting in was turned over. Walter immediately ran over to her, lifted her head and shoulders, then sat her up against his lap. Vivian rushed over to Lynnette, shook her, and slapped her face.

"Lynnette, wake up it's Mommie. Wake up, Lynnette. Lynnette, it's Mommie, wake up."

Vivian ran into the bathroom, wet a small towel in cold water, placed it on Lynnette's forehead, and started to rub her face. "Wake up, Baby, it's Mommie."

Walter felt for a pulse. Satisfied that his daughter was still breathing, he started to rock her back and forth.

"Wake up for Daddy. It's going to be alright. Daddy's here and I'm going to take care of you. Nothing or no one is gonna hurt my baby girl. Daddy loves you and I need you to wake up for me. Come on, Baby girl. Wake up for Daddy."

Lynnette started to stir, and was very hot. She kept her eyes closed but mumbled something. Walter kept on rocking. "That's right, Daddy's here. Wake up for Daddy."

Lynnette opened her eyes and saw her mother. It took her a minute to focus on who Vivian was. When she recognized Vivian, she started to cry and reached for her. Vivian pulled her daughter into her arms and held her tight. Lynnette continued to mumbled words that were not clearly understandable.

"It's okay, Baby. Calm down and tell Mommie what happened."

Lynnette did calm down, but not enough so that they could understand her. She mumbled and pointed toward the dining room table and Walter stood up to see what she was pointing at. He picked up the letter and read the first few words to himself, but when he glanced at the bottom of the letter and saw the grounds for divorce, his eyes grew wide.

"Extreme and repeated mental cruelty?"

When Lynnette heard him, she screamed and jerked herself away from Vivian's arms and began banging her head on the hardwood floor repeatedly. Each time she hit her head, she would cry out Gerald's name. Walter and Vivian grabbed and held her, then Lynnette balled herself up in a fetal position and lay in her mother's arms as if she was inside her womb. Walter ran to the kitchen telephone, dialed emergency, and asked for an ambulance. As he was talking to the operator, he looked at Vivian, saw that she was crying and rocking Lynnette back and forth, and remembered she had high blood pressure. He didn't want to take any chances, so he told the operator to send two ambulances.

Vivian wasn't admitted, but Lynnette had to be. After the nurse gave her a sedative through the I.V. she allowed Vivian and Walter to come into the hospital room. Lynnette was asleep and resting comfortably. Vivian sat on the bed next to Lynnette and began rubbing her hair away from her face.

"What happened to our baby, Walter?"

"Gerald happened to her. Wait til' I see that bastard."

"Walter, please don't do anything crazy. It's obvious Gerald has a problem. Let the Lord deal with him. We have to be here for Lynnette. She's all I'm concerned about. Gerald will get what's coming to him sooner or later and can't nobody get him like God can."

The head physician of Loyola University Emergency walked in with Lynnette's chart in his hand. "Hello, I'm Dr. Trotter and I take it you're Lynnette's parents."

Walter walked over and shook his hand. "Yes. We're Mr. and Mrs. Nelson. What can you tell us about our daughter? What happened to her today?"

Dr. Trotter placed Lynnette's chart on the end of the bed and folded his arms across his chest. "Well, it seems as though Lynnette experienced a nervous breakdown this morning. I gathered from the information you gave to the nurse that she's having marital problems. She's completely dehydrated and I imagine that's because of the amount of tears she sheds. There are a few bruises on the right side of her head. They may have come from her banging her head against the floor. It's likely she'll have a concussion, but we'll have to wait until she wakes up to see. Now she's resting and we're replenishing her fluids through the I.V. With the sedative, she will sleep through the day and night. I'm uh, I'm sorry to say she's lost the baby."

Walter and Vivian looked at each other, then the doctor, then each other again. Vivian stood up from the bed. "There was a baby?"

Dr. Trotter looked puzzled. "Yes. She was beginning her second trimester. She didn't tell you?"

Walter sat down in the chair next to Lynnette. "No. We had no idea she was pregnant. There's so much going on with her that she keeps to herself. My poor baby girl. How are we going to tell her this?"

"Mr. and Mrs. Nelson, you both look exhausted. Lynnette is heavily sedated so she won't wake up at all today. I suggest you go home and get some rest. I'll see you in the morning."

As Dr. Trotter turned to leave, Walter got up and walked over to him.

"Dr. Trotter, do we have to tell her right away about the baby? I mean can't we wait awhile?"

"Mr. Nelson, when she wakes up, she'll feel cramping in her lower abdomen, and she's wearing a pad. She'll know immediately. This is something we can't put off."

Vivian and Walter both thanked the doctor and he left.

"You go on home, Walter. I'm going to stay here overnight with her, just in case she wakes up. I don't want to leave her alone."

Walter kissed Lynnette's hand then kissed Vivian. "Okay, but first I'll stop by her office and let her manager know what's going on. If she wakes up, call me. I don't care what time it is."

Walter left and Vivian took a brush from her purse and got into bed with Lynnette. She brushed her hair a few times then wrapped her arms around her daughter and started to sing in her ear.

"I love you, Mommie loves you. Yes, I do. I sure do love you and Daddy does too."

In the faint distance of her mind, Lynnette heard her mother's voice and her face began to glow as though a ray of light was shining down from somewhere up above.

"THE DEVIL'S SEED IS NOW ABSENT FROM YOUR WOMB."

Vivian saw tears streaming from Lynnette's eyes into her ears. She pulled a tissue from her purse, wiped Lynnette's tears away, and kept on singing. Even though she was heavily sedated, Lynnette was singing her own song.

"God has smiled on me and He has set me free. Oh yes, God has smiled on me and He's been good to me."

She whispered a very quiet, "Thank You."

Vivian whispered back to her. "You're welcome, baby."

Of course Lynnette appreciated her mother being there and wiping her tears away, but she wasn't thanking Vivian at that moment.

Chapter 30

Lynnette was admitted into the hospital on Monday morning. On Tuesday night, she was at her parents home sleeping in her old bedroom. By Wednesday morning, she was back at work. She had mentally blocked out the miscarriage. Vivian begged her to stay home from work and read the pamphlets on dealing with a miscarriage, but Lynnette said she never really got used to being pregnant, and didn't feel as though she'd lost anything. She certainly didn't miss the vomiting and dizziness. Betty tried for hours to convince her to go back home and rest. Lynnette thanked Betty for her concern. However, she said the best thing for her right now was to stay busy. Betty consulted with Dr. Horback who explained that Lynnette was going through a denial period. She said this happens when women miscarry and don't want to think about it. But sooner or later, Lynnette would snap and she would definitely need her family around her for support. Just to satisfy Vivian, she slept in her old bedroom for the rest of the week. By Sunday morning, Lynnette was ready to snap. Not because of the miscarriage, but because of the amount of attention Vivian was forcing on her. For the entire week, Vivian waited on Lynnette hand and foot. She picked out what clothes Lynnette wore to work and ran her bath water every night. She even cut her food into tiny pieces. On Sunday, Vivian insisted that Lynnette allow her to wash and set her hair. Lynnette knew if she didn't go to her own apartment soon, Vivian would surely drive her straight to Nutsville. She asked her father how he managed to stay sane living with Vivian. He told her Vivian is the main reason he's sixty-one years old and still working. Walter, who could've retired ten years ago, knew that if he didn't separate himself from his wife for at least eight hours a day, he too would be on that road to Nutsville.

After her hair was done, Lynnette got dressed for church, kissed her mother goodbye, and told her she would call her when she got to work on Monday. When she opened the front door to leave, Walter called her name.

"Yes, Daddy?"

Walter was coming into the living room from the den. He approached Lynnette and gave her a light nudge on her back. "Let's step onto the porch."

They walked outside, then Walter closed the door behind them. "I don't want your mother to hear us talking. I've been waiting for a chance to be alone with you so we can talk, but Vivian insists on being your shadow. So I figured I'd better catch you before you left for church."

Lynnette looked into her father's face and knew that he was getting ready to make her cry.

"What is it, Daddy?"

Walter placed his hands in his front pockets, inhaled deeply and exhaled. "How are you doing, Baby girl? I mean how are you *really* doing?"

"Daddy, please don't make me cry. It took me almost a half hour to get my face right. I'm on my way to church, can I call you when I get home?"

"No, you can not. It won't kill you to be five minutes late. And what church are you going to anyway?"

"I don't know yet. I was going to decide when I got in the car."

"What? That doesn't make any sense, Lynnette. Why don't you wait for your mother and I to get dressed and go to church with us?"

"Uh, uh. Your Pastor begs too much. He always has to have four or five offerings. And then he wants a five dollar line, a twenty dollar line and a fifty dollar line. I don't feel like sitting through that today."

"So what are you going to do?"

"Daddy, I'm just going to drive around until I get to the first church I see. Is this what you wanted to talk about?"

Walter walked over to the swing and sat down then patted the space next to him. "Come and sit down for a minute."

"Daddy, I don't feel like sitting down and you're making me late for church."

"Baby girl, that's the second time today you told me what you don't feel like doing and I don't like that. Explain to me how you're going to be late getting someplace if you don't know where that place is?"

Lynnette felt the tears coming and opened her purse to get a tissue. "Daddy, please. I don't feel like talking, I just want to go to church."

"That's strike three with the 'I-don't-feel-likes.' Whatever church that you decide to attend this morning will still be standing whenever you get there, I promise you that. Come and sit down. Right now."

Lynnette stood there for a good ten seconds. She wiped the tears that made their appearance and slowly walked over to her father and sat down.

"I don't want to upset you. All I want is to know how you're feeling."

"I'm fine, Daddy. Don't I look fine?"

120

"Yeah, you look great, but I can only see what's exposed. How are you on the inside?"

"I don't know what you want me say, Daddy. I mean, I can tell you I feel good but what's the point? I'd just be wasting my breath because it's not likely that you'd believe me."

Walter grabbed her hand and brought it to his lips and kissed her open palm.

"I love you more than anything in this world, Baby girl. And there is nothing I wouldn't do for you or your mother. You are my heart and my job is to protect my heart."

Lynnette wiped her eyes with the tissue again. "Sniff, sniff"

"Oh Daddy, he hurt me so bad. I thought he loved me, Daddy, I really did. I feel so stupid and used. What's going to happen to me now? What am I gonna do?"

"You're gonna live. That's what you're gonna do. But you're gonna live for Lynnette. You don't need a man to make you feel complete. God completes you. So you're gonna hold your head up, stick your chest out, and walk boldly in the Lord. You're going to go on and live your life to its fullest. It's time for you to reach higher, farther, and deeper than you ever have before. God's got some treasures He's hidden just for you. That means nobody else knows where your treasures are, so they can't get them. They are only for you. Follow God and He will lead you to them."

Lynnette kissed her father's cheek and looked in his eyes. "Thank you, Daddy. You always know what to say to make me feel good."

"Lynnette, I can't apologize for what Gerald has done. Only he can do that. But even if he doesn't, I don't want you to close yourself up and not heal so that God can't send your real husband to you. Don't let Gerald's actions make you bitter toward all men, because not all of us are like Gerald. There are good, kind, and decent men in this world."

"Yes, I know, Daddy, and I have already prayed about that. And I do want to get married again. But believe me, next time I'm gonna make sure he's the one from God."

Walter stood and pulled her up to him. "That's good, Baby, that's what I wanted to hear. You've always been strong, but I just wanted to make sure you were really okay."

She hugged her father again and when she let go, he didn't. She wrapped her arms around him again. He squeezed her tight as if he was hugging her for the last time. "I know I gotta let you go, but I don't want to."

Just then Vivian opened the front door. "What are you two doing out here?"

They let go of the embrace and Lynnette looked at her mother. "Just talking."

"About what?"

Now it was Walter's turn. "Father and daughter stuff."

He winked at Lynnette and gave her hand one last squeeze then went inside.

In the past four months, Lynnette had been through three churches. She didn't want to go back to Mount Vernon although she knew Debra and others would welcome her with open arms. She wanted to move forward in life. She couldn't go back to New Friendship Baptist, because she didn't want to see Melanie's face ever again. She couldn't go back to True Divine Baptist because of Gerald and Simone. So Lynnette decided to drive around and walk in the first church she came upon. While driving she remembered reading an article in the newspaper about a Pastor in Hillside, Illinois who gave away thousands of dollars to his members. He said God came to him in a dream and told him to bless His flock financially. Lynnette knew the name of the church, but not the exact location. She drove to a pay phone and dialed the operator for information. Before Lynnette got to the corner of Frontage Road, she saw the big sign from the expressway that said, "**_Progressive Life-Giving Word Cathedral, Apostle Donald L. Alford, Pastor._**"

Blow Me A Trumpet

This is your day and this is your Father's world. He created it just for you. You are an heir to the universe. Your only boundaries are your own perceptions of potential. You can reach farther than your fingers and leap higher than your doubt. If you lift your head and raise your hands, the clouds will run away. You are kissed. Didn't you know it? Haven't you realized? That's why you are alive to show it. So show up and show off and show out. It is morning!

Never lose that little-girl belief in the impossible. The fantasies of the faithful dispel the myths of the frightened. Somebody blow me a trumpet! The races are about to begin, and the daughters of God are all dressed up. They have stripped themselves of the cares of this world. They have washed away the abuse of their childhood. They have demanded their inheritance, nursed their own babies, strengthened themselves, and prepared their feet to run.

They are sisters of the Cross, survivors of the secrets. They have lain awake trembling and even cried through the night. Some have screamed from bruised lips, assaulted bodies, broken hearts, betrayed trust! But what of the night? That's right, what of it? Haven't you heard? It is morning. Sound the alarm.

Tell the executive to make room for black pumps and tweed skirts on the elevator. They are moving from the poor house to the White House. Fresh out of fear, God's women are on the move.

Loosed women? You'd better believe it. They are loosed from the tragedy of a long and dismal night. They are the daughters of Abraham. They are women with promise. Precious promises are waiting for loosed women who have made themselves ready to take the kingdom by force. No more forbidden fruit for them; they are taking a bite out of life. No more restrictions or inhibitions. Many have been held back by the fear of failure and rejection. Tell the critics the Father says, "Let My Daughter Go!" Only a foolish person would fight a man for his daughter when it is God the Father he will have to fight.

The trumpet has sounded. You are loosed!

God's Divine Revelation

For he who would love life And see good days, Let him refrain his tongue from evil, And his lips from speaking deceit. Let him turn away from evil and do good; Let him seek peace and pursue it. For the eyes of the Lord are on the righteous. And His ears are open to their prayers; But the face of the Lord is against those who do evil. I Peter 3:10-12

Sitting in church, Lynnette felt as though Apostle Alford was a fly that had been following her around because he knew too much of her business. How did he know she had been crying everyday? How did he know she didn't understand why things turned out the way they did? And who told him she left her husband? Who told him these things about her?

"If you know in your heart and spirit that God has brought you out of a bad situation, you must rejoice. It's okay to cry but make sure you are shedding tears of joy and not tears of sorrow. Sometimes we think when God takes something or someone away from us He's punishing us."

She looked around the church and saw about three hundred people, and although Apostle Alford wasn't looking directly at her, she was embarrassed and angry at the same time, embarrassed because everyone in the church now knew she had a bad marriage, angry because the Pastor who called himself an Apostle, singled her out and told her how she should behave.

I don't believe this man is telling my business like this. Lynnette closed her Bible and was getting up to leave. *I gotta find a church where the Pastor won't preach about his members' personal lives.*

A lady sitting next to Lynnette sniffed. Lynnette looked at the lady and saw she was crying. She sat back in her seat and reached in her purse for a tissue and gave it to her.

"Thank you."

Lynnette looked at her tears. "Whatever it is, God will bring you through."

"He already has. It's just that Pastor really spoke to me just now. Until today I was feeling sorry for myself, but God has revealed to me that the situation He brought me out of is actually for my own good."

A man sitting on the pew in front of them jumped up. "Thank You, Lord, for delivering me from alcohol and drugs. Thank You, Lord, Thank You, Jesus."

Someone on the opposite side of the church yelled out. "Hallelujah, praise God for blessing me with a new job where I'm appreciated. Thank You, Lord, for peace of mind."

So many people were jumping, shouting, testifying, and praising God for deliverance, peace, and new beginnings.

Maybe Pastor Alford wasn't only talking about me.

Lynnette opened her Bible again. She wasn't angry or embarrassed anymore as she listened to the Apostle.

"The children of God must learn to trust His direction. We've got to know He won't leave us or forsake us."

The organist started to play. Whenever Pastor's voice rose, he would play just as loudly.

"How many of you know everything that looks good *to* you is not always good *for* you?"

Lynnette could hardly keep her seat. Her feet patted the floor and she rocked back and forth. Apostle Alford kept on preaching.

"Know in your hearts that He is God, it is He who has made us and not we ourselves. Trust Him with all of your heart and lean not to your own understanding. Some of you knew when you got yourselves in the situation to begin with it wasn't pleasing to God. But because you didn't wait for Him to bless you when He was ready to bless you, you found yourselves in a whole lot of trouble. Then you get on your knees and cry out 'Lord, help me out of this, Lord, bless me, Lord, do this and Lord, do that', and when things don't turn out the way you hoped they would, you start whining like a baby, 'Lord, I don't know what I did wrong. Why am I going through this? I'm a good Christian. I did everything I was supposed to do'. Then God says, 'NO YOU DIDN'T.

YOU DIDN'T LISTEN TO ME. I TOLD YOU BEFORE YOU GOT YOURSELF IN THIS MESS TO STAY AWAY FROM IT, NOT TO TOUCH IT, THAT IT WAS NO GOOD FOR YOU AND THAT IT WAS NOT MY WILL'."

Lynnette jumped to her feet. "Preach, Pastor, you are so right. You are speaking the word today."

The organist lost all control. He played louder and Pastor Alford preached louder.

"We always want God to give us what we want when *we* want it. But I'm here to tell you that if God ain't in it, He won't touch it because HE DON'T BLESS NO MESS."

The entire congregation was on its feet. The lady next to Lynnette had passed out long ago. Two nurses were caring for her. Pastor kept on preaching.

"We get ourselves so wrapped up and tangled up in things that God had forewarned us not to get into. But because the lust of our flesh tells us we should have these things, we go ahead and pursue them. How many of you know that it only works for a little while?"

Lynnette yelled out. "I know, I know. Yes, Lord, I know for a fact."

People were shouting, dancing, and praising God, and Lynnette joined right in. Before she knew it she started moving her shoulders and jumping up and down. The organist took over the service and allowed the Holy Spirit to work through him. Lynnette moved out into the aisle and started dancing to the music. Somehow, she lost one of her shoes, but she didn't care. She had to give God His due. She got to the front of the church and the Spirit of God took control of her body. She ran from one side of the church to the other, speaking in tongues, and waving her hands. There were people lain out all over the sanctuary. Some were hugging, crying, and holding each other up. Lynnette was drenched with sweat as she praised God. Apostle Alford came out of the pulpit and ministered to people individually. His elders followed him and his nurse was close by with a bottle of holy oil. Pastor Alford stopped in front of a man, poured oil on his head, and placed his hand on his shoulder.

"Yesterday was your last day of being homeless. Today God is going to bless you with a place to stay."

The man passed out. Pastor Alford stepped over him, walked down the aisle, and called a man and his wife to come to him. He poured oil on both of their heads and handed the microphone to one of his elders to hold up to his mouth. He put his hands on their heads.

"For many years, you have been trying to conceive a child. The doctors told you that you have no womb."

He kept one hand on the husband's head but placed his other hand on the woman's belly.

"In Jesus' name. I cast out any negative word that has been placed upon your belly. Your doctor said no but today Jesus says yes. By the power invested in me, I pronounce you whole, and now you can prepare for your child."

They fell to their knees hand in hand crying and giving God praise.

The church sounded like a basketball stadium at playoff time. Many hands were in the air and many heads were thrown back shouting out praises. Pastor Alford kept on walking and healing people with the help of the Holy Ghost. He was telling them they had been delivered from the enemy's hands. He worked his way towards the front of the church to where Lynnette was. He got to her, told her to raise her hands, and he whispered in her ear.

"Your set time has come."

He poured the oil on her head and put his hands on her shoulders.

"From this day forward, your past is forgotten. God has brought you out of a horrible pit and placed you on high to sit in heavenly places. You will no longer walk in depression, you will walk on it. Surrender your life to Him and let Him have His way with you, because He wants to bless your socks off."

She started jumping in the air and turning around. She lost her other shoe but she didn't care. She was under the anointing of the Holy Spirit as she danced, ran, and spoke in tongues. Apostle Alford got back into the pulpit, looked at his flock, and said with a loud voice, "God has freed you from bondage. There are no more chains holding you. Give Him Glory, Give Him Honor, Give Him Praise, He's Worthy, He's Worthy, He's Worthy."

The entire church let out a shabbach roar and started dancing. Even Pastor Alford was praising and dancing in the pulpit. Lynnette praised and danced so hard she passed out. The next thing she knew, someone had carried her out into the vestibule. When she woke up, nurses were wiping her face with a wet towel and fanning her dry.

Lynnette was exhausted, but she ran to her car shoeless. She prayed all the way to her apartment.

"Lord, just let me make it in the door. I gave You some serious praise this morning and now I'm dead tired. Just a few more blocks, Lord. Please drive this car for me."

She walked in her door at one forty five P.M. By one fifty P.M. she had stripped, kneeled to pray, and buried herself so deep under the cover only her feet could be seen peeking out from beneath. Immediately she fell into a deep sleep.

"WAKE UP MY DAUGHTER."

Lynnette was lying on her back when she opened her eyes. Instantly, she felt sharp stomach pains. She rolled over unto her side and brought her knees to her chest. The pain became stronger and more intense. It felt as though lightning was striking her abdomen. She sat up in bed and noticed that her nightgown was drenched with sweat. It took all that was within her to bring her legs to the side of the bed, place them on the floor, and try to stand. When her feet touched the floor, she put one hand on her stomach and the other on the bed and pushed herself up. When she stood, she felt another lightning bolt that brought her to her knees.

"Oh, God, help me please."

She started to crawl out of the bedroom. *I gotta make it to the bathroom, I gotta throw up.*

Sweat was dripping from her nose, chin, and neck. As she placed one knee ahead of the other, streams of sweat ran into her eyes, and she felt an intense burning that caused her to lose her balance and fall to the floor.

With lightning striking her stomach and fire burning her eyes, she rolled onto her back, put one hand on her belly and the other over her eyes, and cried out, "Jesus, help me."

She started to cry, and when her tears mixed with the sweat in her eyes, she screamed because the fire got hotter. She thought if she could just make it to the bathroom sink and splash cold water in her eyes, everything would be alright. With great determination, she got to her knees and started to crawl again, and as she placed one knee ahead of the other, she was hit with another lightning bolt and fell to the floor.

By this time, she was halfway to the bathroom. No matter how she tried, she didn't have enough strength to get on her knees again. She lay there screaming and crying.

"Help me, Holy Ghost. I don't want to die, not like this."

"YOU ARE NOT DYING, MY DAUGHTER. YOU ARE BEGINNING TO LIVE. IN ORDER FOR ME TO RAISE YOU UP TO WALK, YOU MUST FIRST CRAWL TO ME, FOR I HAVE ALREADY GIVEN YOU THE POWER TO DO SO. ALL YOU HAVE TO DO IS BELIEVE."

Lynnette heard the voice of God, pushed herself up on her hands and knees, and tried with all of her might to move, but she couldn't.

"DON'T GIVE UP, YOU CAN MAKE IT. I AM WITH YOU."

She placed one knee ahead of the other, and another lightning bolt pierced her side, and she screamed, but this time she didn't fall. She cried harder. More sweat ran into her eyes. She screamed again but didn't fall.

"COME UNTO ME FOR YOU ARE BURDENED AND I SHALL GIVE YOU REST."

"I hear You, Lord. I'm trying, but it hurts so bad. I need You to help me."

She prayed for strength and saw she was getting closer to the bathroom. Each time she placed one knee ahead of the other, a lightning bolt would strike, but she was determined to make it to the sink. By the grace of God she managed to crawl into the bathroom. She put one hand on the toilet, and just as she raised herself up, she felt her stomach start to boil. Lynnette could actually hear whatever that was within her belly rumbling around. She placed both hands on the seat of the toilet.

"Oh, God, what's wrong with me?"

As soon as she got the words out, she felt her stomach push its way into her back, and whatever that was within her came up with such a powerful force, it sent her face down into the toilet. Lynnette hadn't eaten anything today, so she couldn't understand what was coming out of her. What she saw in the toilet was not food. She saw black toilet water that had a foul smell.

"Oh my God, oh my God, Jesus, please tell me what's wrong with me. Jesus, help me please."

"I AM CLEANSING YOU OF ALL OF YOUR HURT. THE REJECTION YOU'VE RECEIVED FROM YOUR HUSBAND IS IN YOUR BELLY. YOU HAVE SWALLOWED ALL OF THE PAIN AND DISCOMFORT HE HAS CAUSED YOU. YOU ARE WALK-ING AROUND WITH DEPRESSION, LOW SELF- ESTEEM, AND LONELINESS INSIDE OF YOU."

Lynnette flushed the toilet and braced herself, because another force sent her face into the toilet, and she threw up again.

"Jesus, I can't take no more. Please stop this pain, Lord. It hurts so bad."

"I AM RELEASING ALL OF THE GUILT YOU CARRY INSIDE OF YOU. YOU HAVE BEEN A FAITHFUL WIFE. YOU LOVED YOUR HUSBAND JUST AS I'VE COMMANDED YOU TO DO. I AM CLEANSING YOUR BODY OF EVERY DEMONIC FORCE THAT HAS COME UPON YOU. FROM THIS DAY FORTH, YOU WILL BE FREE IN MY NAME. NO LONGER WILL YOU BE

DEPRESSED, GUILTY, LONELY, OR AFRAID TO MOVE ON.
TODAY I WILL RAISE YOU UP ABOVE EVERYTHING THAT
HAS HINDERED YOU. RIGHT NOW YOU ARE FREE AND
DELIVERED TO LIVE THE LIFE I'VE SET FOR YOU TO LIVE.
YOU WILL WALK IN MY NAME. YOU WILL TALK IN MY
NAME. IT IS IN ME WHERE YOU WILL LIVE, MOVE, AND
HAVE YOUR BEING. I'M ERASING YOUR PAST SO THAT YOU
CAN EMBRACE YOUR FUTURE. EVERY BURDEN HAS BEEN
LIFTED FROM YOUR SHOULDERS. YOUR HUSBAND HAS
DECIDED NOT TO HONOR HIS WEDDING VOWS. HE HAS
ALLOWED HIMSELF TO BE TRICKED BY THE ENEMY. I
WANT YOU TO KNOW THAT THIS IS NOT YOUR FAULT, MY
DAUGHTER. YOU ARE FREE TO LIVE AGAIN. TODAY, I GIVE
YOU THE POWER TO GO ON IN MY NAME. THEREFORE,
YOU CAN GIVE ME EFFECTIVE PRAISE."

Lynnette looked in the toilet at the smelly black water. She flushed it,
and instantly the stomach pains were gone. She fell to the floor.

"Lord, how I give You praise. I magnify Your name, Lord, I lift You up,
Jesus. Thank You for not leaving me and for cleansing my soul. I love You,
Lord."

She grabbed the sink and pulled herself up. She looked in the mirror and
saw that her eyes were red and almost swollen shut.

"Oh God, my eyes. What happened to my eyes?"

"FOR SO LONG YOU COULDN'T SEE THAT I HAVE
WORKED YOUR PROBLEMS OUT FOR YOU. THE ENEMY HAS
BLINDED YOU SO THAT YOU COULDN'T SEE MY LIGHT.
TODAY THROUGH YOUR TEARS, I HAVE SCORCHED EVERY
DEMONIC VISION. THE VISION I'VE SET BEFORE YOUR
EYES IS BRIGHT AND CLEAR. TODAY YOU WILL SEE ME AS
YOUR SAVIOR, YOUR WAY MAKER, AND YOUR STRONG
TOWER. I HAVE OPENED YOUR EYES SO THAT YOU MAY SEE
MY KINGDOM AND YOUR INHERITANCE. KEEP YOUR EYES
FOCUSED ON ME AND I PROMISE TO GIVE YOU AS FAR AS
YOU CAN SEE."

Lynnette fell to her knees again. "Lord, I thank You for giving me a new
vision. I thank You for carrying me through this storm. Thank You for opening my eyes so I can see Your light. I bless You, Jesus."

She stood up, turned on the faucet, and washed her face with cold water.
She brushed her teeth, changed her nightgown, and got back into bed. She
lay down and fell into another deep sleep.

"WAKE UP MY DAUGHTER"

Lynnette opened her eyes and anxiously sat up. Automatically, she put her hand on her belly expecting the lightning to strike, but she felt nothing. She glanced at the clock which read five fifteen A.M. She threw off the cover, ran into the bathroom, and looked in the mirror. Her eyes were bright white. She looked in the toilet and saw that the water was clear. She went back into the bedroom and got on her knees to give God thanks for her new vision and especially for cleansing her soul. After praying she showered and prepared for work. She turned on the radio and heard the words, "God has smiled my way. He's given me another day. I have a brand new life and I'm gonna give Him the praise."

As she was getting dressed, Lynnette looked at her divorce decree that she had framed and hung over her bed. She took it down, read it, then smiled.

"Oh how excellent You are, Lord."

"THIS IS YOUR DIPLOMA. YOU'VE GRADUATED WITH HONORS. COME ON UP A LITTLE HIGHER."

She began to sing along with the radio and clap her hands. She put on her stockings, then she danced. She put on her slip, then she danced. She put on her skirt, then she danced. She put on her blouse, then she danced. She combed her hair, then she danced. She put on her makeup, then she danced. She put on her shoes, then she danced. She grabbed her purse, keys, and Bible, then turned off the radio. She looked up towards heaven with a smile.

"You are an awesome God."

"ALTHOUGH I HAVE OPENED YOUR EYES, YOU HAVEN'T BEGUN TO SEE WHAT I HAVE IN STORE FOR YOU. REMAIN FAITHFUL TO ME AND YOU SHALL RECEIVE YOUR JUST REWARD. ALL I WANT YOU TO DO IS PRAISE ME, SERVE ME, LIVE FOR ME, SHOUT FOR ME, DANCE FOR ME, AND NO GOOD THING WILL I WITHHOLD FROM YOU. I AM ABLE TO DO EXCEEDINGLY ABOVE AND BEYOND ANYTHING YOU COULD EVER ASK. MY KINGDOM IS YOURS, LYNNETTE. ALL YOU'VE GOT TO DO IS PRAISE ME. NOW GO IN PEACE."

Lynnette turned the radio on again and danced out the door, but she never made it to work.

Now the works of the flesh are evident, which are adultery, fornication, uncleanness, lewdness, idolatry, sorcery, hatred, contentions, jealousies, outbursts of wrath, selfish ambitions, dissensions, heresies, envy, murders, drunkenness, revelries, and the like; of which I tell you beforehand, just as I also told you in time past, that those who practice such things will not inherit the kingdom of God. Galatians 5:19-21

He was walking out the front door on his way to work when he felt the earthquake, one that only lasted for just a moment. It came with such a loud blast Gerald thought all the windows had shattered. It shocked and scared him so bad that when the earth shook, he fell forward and bumped his head hard on the doorknob.

"What the heck was that?"

He moaned as he tried to raise himself up to stand. He brought his left hand to his head to feel the bump he knew was already forming. Sure enough, the small pea bump was there and growing larger by the second, he also felt something warm and wet. Gerald brought his hand down to his eyes and saw blood on his fingers. He was dizzy from the fall but carefully stumbled his way into the bathroom and looked inside the medicine cabinet for a bandage and something to wipe away the blood. He cleaned his head as best he could and patched it up, then he lowered the toilet lid and sat down to wait out the dizziness. As soon as he sat down, he heard his next door neighbor scream through the bathroom window.

"My baby, where's my baby? Somebody stole my baby."

Gerald heard this and jumped up immediately, totally forgetting about his concussion as he was running next door to see what happened. As he was staggering to the front door still dizzy and holding his head, it dawned on him that for such a short earthquake, it left his house in shambles. Chairs were thrown about and dishes had fallen to the floor and broken. Even the living room had totally rearranged itself as if it had been sitting in the same position for much too long and decided to give itself a new look, a disastrous look, but definitely a new one. Gerald seemed to be dazed, but somehow he managed to climb over two sofas and a cocktail table to get to the door. When he grabbed the doorknob, he snatched his hand back quickly and yelled out loud, because the doorknob was burning hot and his hand was scorched. He blew on his palm, rubbed it against his jacket, then placed his hand inside his jacket pocket and reached for the doorknob. He felt the intense heat through his cotton jacket, quickly turned the knob, and yanked it opened.

What he saw before him made his heart rise from his chest up to his throat and he had to force himself to swallow it. His eyes were the size of two large eggs. Gerald couldn't believe what he saw, so he closed his eyes real tight, hoping that when he opened them, things would not be as he thought they were. But when he opened them again, the scenery had not changed.

It was red outside, really red. It was like purple and blue mixed together to form the color of dark blood. Gerald felt the heat before he had a

132

chance to step out onto the porch. It was so hot. He felt like he had walked into a sauna fully-clothed and began to sweat immediately. He saw people walking around, looking like the walking dead. Zombies were everywhere. Gerald slowly walked outside and down the porch steps onto the sidewalk. Many cars were in the street banged-up, some were on top of others, and Gerald noticed something very peculiar. Every other car had a driver in it, and he wondered what happened to the drivers in the empty cars. Amazed and confused about what was happening, Gerald was oblivious to the crying, moaning, and screaming all around him. He started walking toward the end of the block and stopped dead in his tracks. He couldn't believe it. Was it possible? No, this is just an illusion. How could a huge 747 airplane be lying in the middle of the street on fire? What happened to its other wing? Better yet, where were the pilots? Gerald saw no one in the cockpit. It was hot, it was red, and it was foggy, because of the many fires that were flaming everywhere. In the street, and even on the sidewalk, cars were lined up like it was rush hour. Cars as well as sport utility vehicles had crashed into trees and run into fire hydrants that were lying on their side, but there was no water. Gerald walked on. To him it appeared as though the world had blown up, or maybe the earth was hit by a missile or some sort of asteroid, and only a few people had survived. It was so hot and humid. He looked up at the sky and saw there was no sun. It was seven o'clock in the morning and there was no sun. Gerald stopped walking again, and thought about what was going on around him.

So that's what happened. That's why it's so hot and that explains all the fires. The sun must've fallen from the sky. What else could it be?

An elderly man walked up to Gerald and held up what appeared to be a woman's nightgown.

"Where is she, where is my wife?"

At that particular moment, Gerald remembered he had parents. He shoved the old man aside and began to run to his parents house three blocks away. It seemed to be about two hundred degrees outside, but Gerald didn't care. He had to get to his parents' house, so he kept on running. He got to their home and was running up the steps to the door when he noticed his mother's longtime friend and neighbor Mrs. Willis, sitting on her porch with her head down. He remembered growing up. He and the rest of the kids on the block referred to her as the Wicked Witch of the West.

She would always sit in her front window and watch and wait for any of them to do something wrong, just so she could tell their parents. This was back in the day when neighbors raised each other's kids. So if you were caught doing something you had no business doing, you could be sure Mrs. Willis was right there in the window to witness it. She wasted no time coming out with either an ironing cord or tree switch, and went to town on whoever wasn't fast enough to outrun her. And if that wasn't bad enough, she would tell their parents when they got home from work, so the kids had another beating to look forward to. And in those days parents never asked questions. They just went to swinging those leather belts.

"Mrs. Willis, are you alright?"

She looked over at Gerald and held up her husband's pajamas.

"He's gone, Richard's gone."

Gerald focused on his parents again and was afraid to go in the house, but he had to know if they were okay. It was so dark and foggy outside. He was at the top of the stairs before he could see the front door. The screen door was off its hinges and no where to be seen, and the front door was ajar. Gerald swallowed hard and found enough courage to walk into the living room and yell for his parents. Their house looked just as his did. The furniture was thrown everywhere, and his mother's crystal had fallen and broken into small pieces. He cleared a path for himself as he walked through the house toward their bedroom. He felt his own body temperature rise fifty degrees. He became more and more nervous as he got closer to their bedroom. The door was closed and he didn't want to open it. He stood outside the door and called for his parents again. When he didn't get an answer that time, he started to cry. He could hear people outside crying and calling for their loved ones.

"Mom, Dad are you okay?" This time he was yelling. He knew all he had to do was open the door, but he didn't want to. He wanted to stand there and wait forever if necessary for his parents to answer him. But Gerald knew. He knew that forever on Earth had ended today. He realized all he was taught as a young boy had come true. His Pastor and mother had taught him well. There were many nights when Thelma read to him from the book of Revelations, and it had gone in one ear and out the other. Why hadn't he listened? He could still hear her words. **"Gerald, you better get right. Jesus is coming and He's coming real soon, so you better get right real quick."**

Gerald would run into the living room and look out the window, up and down the street, then run back to Thelma. **"Well, He ain't here yet."**

She would then say to him, **"Go ahead and be smart young man, but you mark my words, if you keep on doing what you're doing, you and that nasty tongue of yours will be left here all by yourself if you don't get right, because none but the righteous is gonna see God."**

Gerald cried uncontrollably, and for the first time in his life, he tasted fear. Slowly he pushed open the door. The smoke from outside had crept inside the house and made it hard for him to see into the bedroom. He pushed the door open wider, walked to the side of the bed, and what he saw blew his mind. His parents night clothes were lying on the bed as if they were still wearing them. He fell onto the bed crying. He grabbed their pajamas, balled them up to his chest, and lie on the bed. His parents were gone. They had been caught up in the rapture and true enough, he and his nasty tongue were left behind. Outside it was raining fire and brimstone. He cried and cried.

None but the righteous is gonna see God. If you wanna be holy, you've gotta do right. If you wanna see Jesus face to face, get right church, and let's go home.

The End

For my women readers who are big and beautiful like myself who thought, or those of you who still think that we need a man's approval to appreciate who we are, this one's for you!

You Are Somebody

God looked out across eternity. He saw you. He saw everything He had created and everything He would create around you. He saw the specific need on this earth that He would make you to meet. He saw the full set of traits and abilities that you would need in order to complete His purpose for your life. He knew what kind of environment that would be necessary for you to properly develop the gifts He would give you.

God looked...and then He created. He created you. You! And God looked at you and said, "This is good."

Do you have the same opinion of yourself? Do you agree with God's opinion of you? It's important that you appreciate the way God created you because other people are going to treat you the way you treat yourself. They will respect you only to the degree that you respect yourself.

If you are attracting people who don't treat you well, I'm sorry but you are the prime suspect in that case. What kind of message are you sending that allows them to treat you poorly?

In order for people to treat you well, there must be something deep inside of you that sends out a signal saying, "I am somebody because God made me to be somebody. I may not be twenty-one and wear a size seven. I may be seventy-one and wear a size twenty-seven. But I am somebody." When you send out a signal like that, other people pick up on it.

There's something your spirit exudes that gives you presence with others. There's quality of inner strength that makes you attractive. It causes other people to recognize you, to pay attention to you, to ask when you walk into a room, "Who is she?" They won't be asking because your dress is so stunning, but because your character is so magnetic. Projecting that kind of strength is not arrogance or pride. It is healthy self-esteem and the power of God's Spirit within you.

The way you appreciate yourself impacts everything you do. It affects the way you sit in a classroom, or apply for a job, or talk to people at a social function, or go about the ministry God has called you to undertake. It even affects the way you pray and the way you study God's Word. If you think that you are a nobody with no future and no value, you are going to pray with less power and suspect that the promises of God are for everybody else but you.

God wants you to appreciate who He made you to be and to develop what He gave you. He doesn't want you to try to exchange what He gave you for what He gave someone else. You are a unique blend of talents and giftings and character; and you have a unique destiny upon this earth.

You Are Somebody!